CW00522299

TOM TULLY · DAVID SQUE

Roy OF THE Rovers®

THE BEST OF THE 1980s

WHO SHOT ROY RACE?

Writer:
Tom Tully
Artist:
David Sque
Cover Artist: **David Sque**
Design: **Pye Parr**

REBELLION

Creative Director and CEO: **Jason Kingsley**
Chief Technical Officer: **Chris Kingsley**
Head of Books & Comics: **Ben Smith**
Publishing Manager: **Beth Lewis**
Senior Graphic Novel Editor: **Keith Richardson**
Graphic Novel Editors: **Oliver Pickles & Olivia Hicks**
Graphic Design: **Sam Gretton, Oz Osborne & Gemma Sheldrake**
Reprographics: **Joseph Morgan, Emma Denton & Richard Tustian**
Publishing Coordinator: **Owen Johnson**
PR: **Michael Molcher**
PR Assistant: **Rosie Peat**
Roy of the Rovers Brand Manager: **Bobby McGill**
Archivist: **Charlene Taylor**

Originally serialised in **Roy of the Rovers** between 3rd January 1981 – 5th June 1982 and **Roy of the Rovers Annual** 1982. *Roy of the Rovers* is a registered trademark, copyright © 1981, 1982 & 2021 Rebellion Publishing IP Ltd. All rights reserved. No portion of this book may be reproduced without the express permission of the publisher. Names, character, places and incidents featured in the publication are either the product of the author's imagination or used fictitiously. Any resemblance to actual persons, living or dead (except for satirical purposes) is entirely coincidental.

Published by Rebellion,
Riverside House, Osney Mead, Oxford, OX2 0ES, UK.
www.rebellionpublishing.co.uk

Printed by Replika Press PVT LTD in India
First Printing: June 2021
10 9 8 7 6 5 4 3 2 1

ISBN: 978-1-78108-896-8

www.royoftherovers.com

ROY OF THE ROVERS

MELCHESTER ROVERS

"...ROY'S PLAYING SOME KIND OF JOKE ON US! HE MUST BE!"

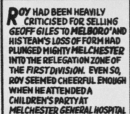

ROY HAD BEEN HEAVILY CRITICISED FOR SELLING GEOFF GILES TO MELBORO' AND HIS TEAM'S LOSS OF FORM HAD PLUNGED MIGHTY MELCHESTER INTO THE RELEGATION ZONE OF THE FIRST DIVISION. EVEN SO, ROY SEEMED CHEERFUL ENOUGH WHEN HE ATTENDED A CHILDREN'S PARTY AT MELCHESTER GENERAL HOSPITAL . . . A PARTY WHICH WAS BEING TELEVISED!

... AND EVEN THOUGH WE'RE THIRD FROM BOTTOM, I'VE GOT A CHAP IN MIND WHO COULD MAKE IT A HAPPY NEW YEAR FOR US!

QUIET, EVERYONE! ROY'S GOING TO REVEAL THE NAME OF THE STAR PLAYER THAT HE'S BOUGHT TO REPLACE GEOFF GILES!

I'VE ALREADY AGREED TERMS WITH OLDFIELD AND HE SHOULD BE SIGNING ON THE DOTTED LINE IN A FEW DAYS! AS A MATTER OF FACT, I'VE GOT A PICTURE OF HIM!

I'M SURE YOU'LL ALL RECOGNISE...

... NAT GOSDEN!

WH-WHAAAAAT?

A COUPLE OF LOCAL REPORTERS, WHO WERE ATTENDING THE PARTY, COULD HARDLY BELIEVE THEIR EARS!

ISN'T THE THE PLAYER THAT THE OLDFIELD FANS HAVE NICKNAMED 'GRANDAD'?

THAT'S RIGHT...

... ROY'S PLAYING SOME KIND OF JOKE ON US! HE MUST BE!

BUT, A DAY OR TWO LATER...

SPORTS

RACE PINS HOPE ON 35 YEAR OLD VETERAN!

... FOOTBALL NEWS ...

FREE TRANSFER FOR 'GRANDAD' GOSDEN!

GLOBE

'I RECKON I'VE GOT THREE GOOD YEARS LEFT IN ME' SAYS FORMER ENGLAND DYNAMO!

AN EVEN BIGGER CROWD OF REPORTERS AND PHOTOGRAPHERS GATHERED OUTSIDE MELCHESTER STADIUM, A WEEK LATER . . .

ELCHESTER R.F.C

HERE HE COMES NOW!

IN THAT BEATEN-UP OLD VAN? I DON'T BELIEVE IT!

IT CAN'T BE GOSDEN!

BUT IT WAS!

EEE! THEY'RE MAKING A REAL FUSS OF US, AREN'T THEY, NAT?

AYE, WELL... IT'S A BIG CLUB, LASS! ALWAYS IN THE HEADLINES!

NEXT WEEK: AMID MASSED JEERING, NAT GOSDEN MAKES HIS DEBUT FOR ROVERS!

ROY OF THE ROVERS

MELCHESTER ROVERS

IT WAS ONE OF THE MOST BREATHTAKING AND GREATEST SAVES EVER SEEN!

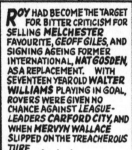

ROY HAD BECOME THE TARGET FOR BITTER CRITICISM FOR SELLING MELCHESTER FAVOURITE, GEOFF GILES, AND SIGNING AGEING FORMER INTERNATIONAL, NAT GOSDEN, AS A REPLACEMENT. WITH SEVENTEEN YEAR OLD WALTER WILLIAMS PLAYING IN GOAL, ROVERS WERE GIVEN NO CHANCE AGAINST LEAGUE-LEADERS CARFORD CITY, AND WHEN MERVYN WALLACE SLIPPED ON THE TREACHEROUS TURF . . .

THE KID CAME OUT TO NARROW THE ANGLE... BUT SAMMY'S SLIPPED THE BALL AROUND HIM!

MELCHESTER ARE ONE GOAL DOWN ALREADY!

BUT, AMAZINGLY...

NO! WHAT A RECOVERY!

WALTER'S GOT IT!

AS THE YOUNG 'KEEPER LEAPT TO HIS FEET...

LOOK! HE'S STILL CLUTCHING THE BALL IN ONE HAND... LIKE IT WAS AN ORANGE!

RIGHT-WING, WALLY! LET IT GO!

AND...

WHAT A THROW — STRAIGHT TO RACEY'S FEET!

I'M BEGINNING TO SEE WHY ROY'S GOT SO MUCH FAITH IN THE KID!

TAKE HIM OUT, CARFORD!

BUT ROY DIDN'T WAIT TO BE 'TAKEN OUT'!

HE'S LASHED IT INTO THE CROWD!

ROY, FOR PETE'S SAKE! WHAT THE HECK WAS THAT IN AID OF?

MERVYN WALLACE! THE REF WON'T ALLOW HIM TO BE TREATED UNTIL THE BALL IS OUT OF PLAY!

GET UP, WALLACE! YOU ONLY FELL OVER!

IT'S A BAD ONE, TOO! I'D BETTER GET WARMED UP, TAFFY! YOUNG MERVYN'S DONE A HAMSTRING, BY THE LOOK OF IT!

I'LL BE THE JUDGE OF THAT! YOU HANG ON A MINUTE, NAT!

ROY OF THE ROVERS

MELCHESTER ROVERS

"WHAT A DUMMY! HE'S TURNED THEM INSIDE OUT..."

MELCHESTER ROVERS WERE FIGHTING TO GET OUT OF THE RELEGATION ZONE AND ROY HAD SHOCKED HIS FANS BY SIGNING AGEING MIDFIELDER, NAT 'GRANDAD' GOSDEN, AND PUTTING SEVENTEEN-YEAR-OLD WALTER WILLIAMS IN GOAL. BUT THE NEWCOMERS HELPED ROY TO GRAB A BRILLIANT, OPENING GOAL AGAINST LEAGUE-LEADERS CARFORD CITY...

ROVERS! ROVERS!

COME ON, CITY... SORT IT OUT! WE'RE LETTING AN OLD MAN MAKE US LOOK SILLY!

LET'S GET THAT GOAL BACK!

ROARED ON BY THEIR FANS, CARFORD MOUNTED A FURIOUS COUNTER-ATTACK!

OHHHH! JIMMY SLADE'S BEEN CAUGHT OUT OF POSITION!

MELCHESTER'S RIGHT FLANK IS WIDE OPEN!

A FIRST-TIME CROSS WAS MET WITH A BULLET OF A HEADER!

YOUNG WILLIAMS HAS DONE IT AGAIN! WHAT A SAVE!

BUT THE BALL'S LOOSE...

...GET IN THERE, CITY!

IT'S YOURS, GOSDEN! CLEAR IT! WHACK IT INTO THE CROWD!

BUT...

WHAT THE—?

GOSDEN'S CLEARED IT, ALL RIGHT... STRAIGHT BACK UP THE PARK!

IT'S HEADING FOR PACO DIAZ!

THE SPANISH SUPERSTAR MADE GOOD USE OF THE TREACHEROUS, GREASY TURF...

NNNNNF!

GAH!

WHAT A DUMMY! HE'S TURNED THEM INSIDE OUT...

...AND KNOCKED IT INSIDE TO ROY!

CLOSE HIM DOWN, CITY! DON'T LET HIM SHOOT!

BUT ROY DELIBERATELY STEPPED OVER THE BALL AND...

VERNON ELIOT.... IT'S THERE!

TWO-NIL TO MELCHESTER!

HURAAAAAAAAY!

EXPECTING THEIR TEAM TO BE THRASHED, THE MELCHESTER FANS WERE WILD WITH DELIGHT. AT HALF-TIME...

SIGNING HIM ON WAS A STROKE OF GENIUS! AND DON'T FORGET WHO SIGNED HIM!

WELL PLAYED, 'GRANDAD' GOSDEN!

ALL TOGETHER NOW — ROY RACE!

ROY RACE! THE GREATEST MANAGER IN THE WORLD!

IT TAKES A MAN OF COURAGE TO SIGN A THIRTY-FIVE-YEAR-OLD VETERAN...

...AND PUT A KID IN GOAL!

BUT WALTER WILLIAMS AND NAT GOSDEN COULDN'T BE EVERYWHERE. SOON AFTER THE RESTART...

AA-AAACH!

DUNCAN McKAY'S MADE A MESS OF THAT HEADER!

HE'S GIVEN IT TO ONE OF THE CITY FORWARDS...

THE CARFORD PLAYER UNLEASHED A HOPEFUL, FIRST-TIME VOLLEY...

IT'S HIT THE UPRIGHT...

...AND REBOUNDED INTO THE NET! IT'S THERE!

WAHOOOOOO!

WE'RE BACK IN THE GAME!

THE VOICE OF NAT GOSDEN RANG CALMLY THROUGH THE PANDEMONIUM...

NO NEED TO FRET, LADS! THEY'LL NOT SCORE SUCH A LUCKY GOAL FOR THE REST OF THE SEASON! WE'RE STILL IN THE DRIVING SEAT!

LISTEN TO 'GRANDAD'! WHAT DOES HE KNOW ABOUT IT?

BUT AS THE GAME GREW TO A FEVER-PITCH OF EXCITEMENT...

GOSDEN'S SHOWING HIS EXPERIENCE NOW! LOOK AT HIM HOLDING THE BALL!

HE'S DELIBERATELY SLOWING DOWN THE GAME — GIVING THE ROVERS TIME TO RECOVER!

AND SUDDENLY...

WHAT A BALL... AND ROY'S ANTICIPATED IT! HE'S AWAY! HE'S GOT A GREAT CHANCE!

MAKE IT SAFE, RACEY! SHOW THEM THAT MELCHESTER ARE ON THE WAY UP AGAIN!

NEXT WEEK'S ACTION WILL TAKE YOUR BREATH AWAY! DON'T MISS IT!

My marks out of ten for this story:

ROY OF THE ROVERS

24th JANUARY, 1981 EVERY MONDAY

15p

©IPC Magazines Ltd., 1981

Australia 40c., New Zealand 40c., Malaysia $1.20.

NEXT WEEK: ROY ORDERS A SPECIAL TRAINING SESSION!

My marks out of ten for this story:

ROY OF THE ROVERS

MELCHESTER ROVERS

ROY'S REPLY TO ALL THE INSULTS SHOCKED EVERYONE!

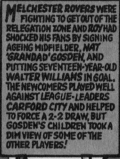

MELCHESTER ROVERS WERE FIGHTING TO GET OUT OF THE RELEGATION ZONE AND ROY HAD SHOCKED HIS FANS BY SIGNING AGEING MIDFIELDER, NAT 'GRANDAD' GOSDEN, AND PUTTING SEVENTEEN-YEAR-OLD WALTER WILLIAMS IN GOAL. THE NEWCOMERS PLAYED WELL AGAINST LEAGUE-LEADERS CARFORD CITY AND HELPED TO FORCE A 2-2 DRAW, BUT GOSDEN'S CHILDREN TOOK A DIM VIEW OF SOME OF THE OTHER PLAYERS!

DIDN'T YOU HEAR HER, GOSDEN? THAT KID OF YOURS JUST INSULTED ME! SHE SAID I WAS USELESS!

AND ME! WHAT ARE YE GOING TO DO ABOUT IT, NAT?

NOTHING! I'VE ALWAYS ENCOURAGED OUR EMMA TO SPEAK HER MIND!

WELL, IT MUST BE FULL OF RUBBISH! SHE SHOULDN'T BE IN HERE, ANYWAY!

AYE! WHAT DO YOU RECKON, ROY?

ER—

I RECKON YOUNG EMMA KNOWS HER FOOTBALL! HEH, HEH!

WHAAAAAT?

YOU MEAN ...YOU AGREE WITH HER?

TO A CERTAIN EXTENT! SOME OF US ARE OUT OF FORM! EVEN THE PLAYERS OF MIGHTY MELCHESTER HAVE TO GO THROUGH A BAD PATCH, FROM TIME TO TIME! BUT I'M SURE WE'LL FIGHT OUR WAY OUT OF IT!

OF COURSE YOU WILL! AFTER ALL, YOU TOOK A POINT FROM THE LEAGUE LEADERS ...WHICH ISN'T SO BAD FOR A TEAM THAT'S PLAYING LIKE A BUNCH OF NOVICES!

TH-THAT'S JUST WHAT I WAS GOING TO SAY!

APART FROM NAT GOSDEN AND HIS 'CLAN', NO ONE ELSE COULD THINK OF ANYTHING TO SAY!

SEE YOU IN THE SUPPORTERS' CLUB, DAD! WE'RE GOING TO PLAY ON THE SPACE INVADERS MACHINE!

RIGHT, ERNIE...

...YOU WATCH YOUR BROTHER AND SISTERS DON'T GET INTO ANY TROUBLE...

AS THE CHILDREN VANISHED, A CRY FROM JIMMY SLADE BROKE THE DISBELIEVING HUSH...

HEY, LOOK...THE RESULTS OF THE OTHER GAMES ARE COMING THROUGH!

4.42 PORTDEAN 2 RED...
4.42 MILBORO 1 KINGS
4.43 KELBURN 2 N VAL
4

KELBURN WON AGAIN...

ROY OF THE ROVERS

MELCHESTER ROVERS

DESPITE HOLDING LEAGUE LEADERS *CARFORD CITY* TO A DRAW, *MELCHESTER ROVERS* WERE STILL IN DANGER OF RELEGATION, AND *ROY* ORDERED THE PLAYERS TO REPORT FOR SUNDAY TRAINING. THIS MADE HIM UNPOPULAR WITH HIS WIFE, PENNY . . . AND AFTER A FURIOUS ARGUMENT, ROY ARRIVED AT A NEAR-DESERTED TRAINING GROUND . . .

NAT GOSDEN AND HIS KIDS — THE *ONLY* PEOPLE WHO HAVE TURNED UP!

SO I'VE EVEN LOST THE CONFIDENCE OF MY *PLAYERS,* NOW!

ROY'S DECISION TO SIGN THE VETERAN MIDFIELDER HAD BEEN A BIG SUCCESS, BUT HE FELT LITTLE CONSOLATION NOW . . .

ER . . . LOOKS AS IF YOUNG ERNIE IS GOING TO FOLLOW IN YOUR FOOTSTEPS, NAT!

HOPE SO, ROY! WE'RE JUST HAVING A BIT OF A KICK-ABOUT TO PASS THE TIME, LIKE . . .

. . . THE OTHER LADS AREN'T AROUND AT THE MOMENT, AS YOU CAN SEE!

ONLY *TOO* WELL! NOT EVEN BLACKIE GRAY, WHO'S SUPPOSED TO BE MY BEST PAL! I — I GUESS THAT'S IT! I MIGHT AS WELL *RESIGN!*

MY MISTAKE! HERE THEY COME NOW!

UUUUH?

MOST OF THEM GOT HERE *TOO* EARLY, SO THEY DECIDED TO GO FOR A JOG THROUGH MELTON RIDGES!

WELL, I'LL BE . . .

'MORNING, RACEY!

HOPE THIS SUNDAY TRAINING LARK DOESN'T CATCH ON! I ALMOST OVERSLEPT!

ME, TOO, MAN! YOU'RE NOT VERY POPULAR IN MY HOUSEHOLD AT THE MOMENT, ROY . . .

. . . BUT LIKE I TOLD THE WIFE — ROY ISN'T DOING THIS FOR *HIS OWN* BENEFIT!

IT'S FOR ALL OF US! AND THE *CLUB* HE'S SERVED FOR MOST OF HIS LIFE . . .

. . . MIGHTY MELCHESTER! SO HERE WE ARE, LADDIE!

ROY WAS SO MOVED, HE WAS AT A LOSS FOR WORDS . . .

ER . . . ANYTHING WRONG, SKIPPER?

EH? . . . I . . . I MEAN . . . *NO! NO!* EVERYTHING'S JUST FINE, BLACKIE! I — ER GUESS WE MIGHT AS WELL GET DOWN TO IT!

AS MORE PLAYERS ARRIVED, ROY WAS ABLE TO STAGE A FULL-SCALE PRACTICE MATCH... THE FIRST-TEAM AGAINST RESERVES AND APPRENTICES...

THAT'S IT... JUST KNOCK THE BALL AROUND! ENJOY YOURSELVES!

LET'S TRY AND RECAPTURE OUR OLD, INSTINCTIVE 'TOUCH' ON THE BALL!

CHARLIE CARTER—WHO HAD BEEN DROPPED FOLLOWING A LOSS OF FORM, WAS PLAYING IN GOAL FOR THE RESERVES...

SAAAAAAVED, CHARLIE!

BUT THAT WAS A BRILLIANT SNAP-SHOT FROM PACO DIAZ! SPUR-OF-THE-MOMENT STUFF...WHICH IS WHAT HE'S BEST AT!

...AND THAT WAS A GREAT RUN, VIC GUTHRIE! YOU CAME OUT OF NOWHERE, JUST LIKE YOU USED TO!

CHARLIE WAS EVENTUALLY BEATEN BY A TYPICAL, FOUR-MAN MOVE...

NICE ONE, BLACKIE! THAT'S HOW WE USED TO SCORE GOALS... EVERYONE GETTING INTO THE ACT!

CHARLIE HAD NO CHANCE!

BUT 'THE CAT' IS BACK ON FORM, IT SEEMS! IN FACT, YOU'RE ALL PLAYING WITH A FREEDOM AND FLAIR THAT'S BEEN MISSING!

IT'S GOING TO BE A PROBLEM PICKING A TEAM FOR THE F.A. CUP MATCH AGAINST ROTHERTON, ON SATURDAY...

... BUT THAT'S THE KIND OF 'PROBLEM' I LIKE!

LATER...

THE TRAINING SESSION WENT SO WELL, WE WERE ABLE TO FINISH EARLY, WHICH OUGHT TO PLEASE PENNY!

I'M SURE SHE DIDN'T MEAN... UUUH? THAT'S FUNNY! PENNY'S CAR ISN'T IN THE GARAGE!

THE HOUSE SEEMS... DESERTED!

BUT IT CAN'T BE!

SURELY SHE WOULDN'T WALK OUT ON ME AT A TIME LIKE THIS?

HAS SHE? WOULD SHE? YOU CAN FIND OUT NEXT WEEK!

My marks out of ten for this story:

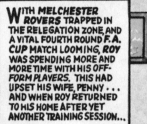

THERE'S A SENSATIONAL GOAL IN NEXT WEEK'S INSTALMENT!

My marks out of ten for this story:

SEE ANOTHER STUNNING GOAL IN NEXT WEEK'S ISSUE!

IT REALLY WAS ROY OF THE ROVERS STUFF!

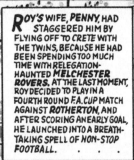

ROY'S WIFE, PENNY, HAD STAGGERED HIM BY FLYING OFF TO CRETE WITH THE TWINS, BECAUSE HE HAD BEEN SPENDING TOO MUCH TIME WITH RELEGATION-HAUNTED MELCHESTER ROVERS. AT THE LAST MOMENT, ROY DECIDED TO PLAY IN A FOURTH ROUND F.A. CUP MATCH AGAINST ROTHERTON, AND AFTER SCORING AN EARLY GOAL, HE LAUNCHED INTO A BREATH-TAKING SPELL OF NON-STOP FOOTBALL.

...TWO...THREE...FOUR! WHAT A RUN!

RACEY'S LIKE A WHIRLWIND! HE'S PLAYING AS IF FOOTBALL IS GOING OUT OF FASHION!

THE ROTHERTON DEFENCE CRUMBLED BEFORE ROY'S INCREDIBLE, ONE-MAN ONSLAUGHT...

NOW GET IT ACROSS, ROY! JIMMY SLADE IS AT THE FAR POST!

COVER ME, ROTHERTON!

GLANCING UP, ROY SAW THAT THE ROTHERTON 'KEEPER WAS STRAYING OFF HIS LINE...

SORRY, JIMMY! THIS GUY IS ASKING TO GET HIMSELF 'LOBBED'...

...SO I'LL OBLIGE HIM!

OH, N-NO...

TWO-NIL....IT'S THERRRRRRE!

AND RACEY STILL HASN'T STOPPED! LOOK AT HIM CHARGING BACK DOWN THE PARK!

HE CAN'T WAIT TO GET STUCK INTO ROTHERTON AGAIN!

EVERY TIME THE MELCHESTER SKIPPER GOT THE BALL, IT WAS PANIC-STATIONS FOR THE VISITORS!

OHHHHH! THAT TOOK THE PAINT OFF THE CROSSBAR!

HOW THE HECK DID HE GET TO THAT?

THEN!

ROY'S GOING TO MAKE A SUBSTITUTION! HE'S SIGNALLING TO MERVYN WALLACE TO GET WARMED UP!

BUT WHO IS HE GOING TO PULL OFF?

BE SURE TO FIND OUT WHAT'S HAPPENED TO ROY IN NEXT WEEK'S ISSUE!

ROY OF THE ROVERS

7th MARCH, 1981 EVERY MONDAY

15p

© IPC Magazines Ltd., 1981

Australia 40c., New Zealand 40c., Malaysia $1.20.

CONTINUED FROM FRONT COVER

NEXT WEEK: A POSSIBLE SOLUTION TO ROY'S DOMESTIC PROBLEM!

ROY'S WIFE, PENNY, HAD STAGGERED HIM BY FLYING OFF TO CRETE WITH THE TWINS, BECAUSE HE HAD BEEN SPENDING TOO MUCH TIME WITH RELEGATION-HAUNTED MELCHESTER ROVERS. DURING AN F.A. CUP MATCH AGAINST ROTHERTON, THE EXHAUSTED ROY FELL ASLEEP IN THE TREATMENT ROOM, AFTER GIVING THE ROVERS A TWO-GOAL LEAD. THEN, IN THE LAST SECONDS OF THE GAME . . .

FIVE-NIL! THE ROVERS ARE SWAMPING THEM!

WE WANT SIX! WE WANT SIX!

PACO DIAZ OBLIGED THE MELCHESTER FANS, WITH YET ANOTHER MASTERLY TOUCH . . .

HE'S PUSHED IT THROUGH THE KEEPER'S LEGS!

THAT'S PACO'S HAT-TRICK!

IT WAS ALSO THE LAST KICK OF THE GAME . . .

THERE'S THE WHISTLE . . . AND THERE'S ROY! HE'S WOKEN UP AT LAST!

YOU'VE MISSED ALL THE FUN, SKIPPER!

AYE, SORRY ABOUT THAT, BUT IT'S NICE TO KNOW THAT YOU CAN TAKE CARE OF YOURSELVES!

LOOKS AS IF WE'LL HAVE TO START TAKING CARE OF YOU, ROY . . .

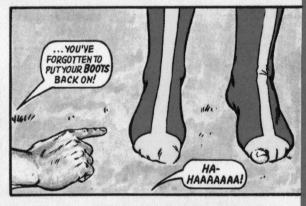

. . . YOU'VE FORGOTTEN TO PUT YOUR BOOTS BACK ON!

HA-HAAAAAAA!

ANYWAY, YOU'VE OBVIOUSLY FOUND THE PERFECT ANSWER TO ALL YOUR PROBLEMS, ROY . . . YOU JUST SLEEP ON THEM!

IT'S NO JOKE, BLACKIE . . .

. . . MISSING OUR BEST RESULT OF THE SEASON BECAUSE I WAS HAVING A NAP!

ROY THOUGHT THAT THE ROVERS DIDN'T KNOW THE REAL REASON FOR PENNY'S ABSENCE . . .

I'M BEGINNING TO WISH I HADN'T TOLD PENNY TO TAKE A LITTLE, ER . . . HOLIDAY! WASHING AND COOKING FOR YOURSELF CAN BE PRETTY TIRING, YOU KNOW!

SO WHY DON'T YOU COME ROUND TO MY PLACE FOR A BITE TO EAT?

NEXT WEEK: "NOT EVEN ROY RACE CAN GET AWAY WITH THAT!"

My marks out of ten for this story:

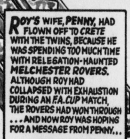

ROY'S WIFE, PENNY, HAD FLOWN OFF TO CRETE WITH THE TWINS, BECAUSE HE WAS SPENDING TOO MUCH TIME WITH RELEGATION-HAUNTED MELCHESTER ROVERS. ALTHOUGH ROY HAD COLLAPSED WITH EXHAUSTION DURING AN F.A. CUP MATCH, THE ROVERS HAD WON THROUGH ...AND NOW ROY WAS HOPING FOR A MESSAGE FROM PENNY...

THE POSTMAN! THERE'S JUST GOT TO BE A CARD, OR SOMETHING, FROM PENNY!

BUT...

NOT A THING...APART FROM THE USUAL MAIL.... HUH? WAIT A MINUTE! THIS LOOKS LIKE HER MOTHER'S HANDWRITING...

ROY WAS RIGHT...

WE'LL, I'LL BE...

Dear Roy
Just to let you know that I have heard from Penny. She's having a wonderful time and the twins are as brown as berries! In haste,
Audrey

...I MUST BE BARMY— WORRYING ABOUT OTHER PEOPLE, WHEN THEY COULDN'T GIVE TWO HOOTS ABOUT ME! IT'S TIME YOU STARTED THINKING ABOUT YOURSELF, RACEY!

SO ROY CLEANED UP THE HOUSE...

...HAD A SHAVE FOR THE FIRST TIME IN TWO DAYS...

...AND PUT ON HIS BEST SUIT!

THAT'S IT...

...I'M READY FOR ANYTHING NOW ...INCLUDING BRADPORT!

LATER, AT MELCHESTER STADIUM, WHERE THE ROVERS WERE WAITING TO BOARD THE TEAM COACH FOR THE LONG TRIP TO THE NORTH-EAST...

OOOOH, I SAY! DO WE HAVE TO BOW TO IT FIRST?

IT...IT'S DAZZLING MY EYES!

ALL RIGHT! CUT THE WISECRACKS...

...ANYONE WOULD THINK WE WERE TOP OF THE LEAGUE! I HOPE YOU CAN STILL GRIN LIKE IDIOTS IF WE GET RELEGATED TO THE SECOND DIVISION!

GULP!

NOT EVEN NOEL BAXTER COULD FIND ANYTHING TO LAUGH AT DURING THE JOURNEY TO BRADPORT...

...FORGET THAT SIX-NIL VICTORY IN THE CUP! YOU'LL ALL BE PLAYING FOR YOUR PLACES, TOMORROW!

PHEW! LET'S HOPE HE CALMS DOWN! OR WE'LL BE UNDER MORE PRESSURE FROM RACEY THAN BRADPORT!

BUT AS THE ROVERS RAN OUT, THE FOLLOWING AFTERNOON!

'OH, WHERE, OH WHERE HAS MY PENNY GONE, OH, WHERE, OH, WHERE CAN SHE BEEEEEEE?'

WHAT THE—?

GOOD GRIEF! LISTEN TO THAT!

HA! HAAAAAAA!

HOW THE HECK DID THE BRADPORT FANS FIND OUT ABOUT ROY'S LITTLE DOMESTIC PROBLEM?

RUMOURS, I GUESS...

...RACEY'S ANGRIER THAN EVER, NOW... READY TO BLOW HIS TOP!

THE EXPLOSION CAME SOON AFTER THE KICK-OFF...

FOUUUUL! NOT EVEN ROY RACE CAN GET AWAY WITH THAT!

AAAAAAGH!

A PROFESSIONAL FOUL, ROY! YOU KNOW I CAN'T IGNORE IT!

HE'S CAUTIONED! ROY RACE HAS BEEN BOOKED!

HURAA-AAAAY!

AND TO MAKE MATTERS WORSE!

GOOOAAAAL! WE'VE KNOCKED IT IN FROM THE FREE-KICK!

THANKS A MILLION, RACEY!

MELCHESTER FOUGHT BACK FIERCELY...AND AFTER A SPELL OF CONSTANT PRESSURE LATE IN THE SECOND-HALF...

JIMMY SLADE'S EQUALISED! WAHOO-OOO!

THAT'S THE STUFF, ROVERS!

ONE MORE AND WE'RE OUT OF THE BOTTOM THREE!

BUT THE GAME ENDED IN A 1-1 DRAW...

THAT POINT WON'T BE ENOUGH TO LIFT US OUT OF THE RELEGATION ZONE... NOT EVEN IF THE CLUBS ABOVE US LOSE!

NEVER MIND, WE'RE STILL IN THE EUROPEAN CUP! LET'S HOPE WE CAN DO BETTER AGAINST ZALMO, ON WEDNESDAY NIGHT!

THE ROVERS HAD LOST THE FIRST LEG, 2-0, IN THEIR FOURTH ROUND EUROPEAN CUP-TIE AGAINST THE SWEDISH CHAMPIONS...

...AND I DON'T FANCY OUR CHANCES ONE BIT...

...NOT WHILE ROY IS IN THIS MOOD! FOR PETE'S SAKE... COME HOME, PENNY!

NEXT WEEK: MORE TROUBLE FOR ROVERS ... IN THE EUROPEAN CUP!

My marks out of ten for this story!

ROY OF THE ROVERS

MELCHESTER ROVERS

ROY WAS DRIVING HIS PLAYERS HARDER THAN HE'D EVER DONE BEFORE!

ROY'S WIFE, PENNY, HAD FLOWN OFF TO CRETE WITH THE RACE TWINS, IN PROTEST AT THE AMOUNT OF TIME HE WAS SPENDING WITH RELEGATION-HAUNTED MELCHESTER ROVERS. INFURIATED BY SUGGESTIONS THAT HE WAS LOSING CONTROL OF THE CLUB, ROY HELD YET ANOTHER TRAINING SESSION ON THE EVE OF A FOURTH ROUND EUROPEAN CUP MATCH AGAINST SWEDISH CHAMPIONS ZALMO . . .

THE ONLY WAY TO WIN FOOTBALL MATCHES IS TO SCORE GOALS... SO WE'RE GOING TO TRY SOME PLAIN, OLD-FASHIONED SHOOTING PRACTICE!

WHEN I SHOUT A NUMBER, I WANT TO SEE THAT BALL HITTING THE APPROPRIATE SQUARE...DEAD-CENTRE! OKAY?

...SEVEN!

TOUGH LUCK, BLACKIE...

...LEFT A BIT AND DOWN A BIT!

OR MAYBE YOU'D ALL LIKE TO GET A BIT CLOSER! THAT WAS TERRIBLE! NOW LET'S TRY NUMBER THREE, JIMMY SLADE...

HOW'S THAT, BOSS?

EXCELLENT... FOR SOMEONE WITH TWO LEFT FEET! I CAN SEE WE'VE GOT A LONG SESSION AHEAD OF US!

TAFFY MORGAN AND BEN GALLOWAY, THE CLUB'S GENERAL MANAGER, WERE WATCHING THE SHOOTING SESSION . . .

...RUBBISH! TRY NUMBER NINE!

I'VE NEVER SEEN HIM DRIVING THEM SO HARD, TAFFY! AND YOU KNOW WHY, DON'T YOU?

AYE...

...ROY'S TRYING TO SHOW EVERYONE THAT HE'S STILL THE BEST MAN FOR THE JOB...DESPITE HIS LITTLE, ER, DOMESTIC PROBLEM!

MAYBE HE'S TRYING TOO HARD! IT COULD BE THE PLAYERS WHO SUFFER IN THE LONG RUN!

AS THE TWO-HOUR SLOG AT LAST CAME TO AN END . . .

OOOHHH! HOPE I'VE GOT ENOUGH ENERGY LEFT FOR ZALMO!

COME BACK, PENNY... THAT'S WHAT I SAY!

NO CHANCE, LADDIE! ROY'S AS STUBBORN AS THEY COME...

WHY IS ROY HEADING FOR THE BENCH? FIND OUT NEXT WEEK!

My marks out of ten for this story:

ROY OF THE ROVERS

MELCHESTER ROVERS

ROY'S WIFE, PENNY, HAD FLOWN OFF TO CRETE WITH THE RACE TWINS, IN PROTEST AT THE AMOUNT OF TIME HE WAS SPENDING WITH RELEGATION-HAUNTED *MELCHESTER ROVERS.* IN THE FOURTH ROUND OF THE *EUROPEAN CUP,* AGAINST *ZALMO,* ROY'S PRESSURE-TACTICS RECEIVED AN EARLY BLOW WHEN THE *SWEDES* BROKE AWAY AND ADDED TO THEIR 2-0 LEAD. *THEN* . . .

ROY'S *PANICKED!* THAT GOAL *SHOOK* HIM SO MUCH, HE'S GOING TO MAKE A *SUBSTITUTION* ALREADY!

BETTER GET YOUR TRACK SUIT OFF, STEVE . . .

BUT ROY HAD NO INTENTION OF BRINGING ON STEVE NAYLOR! HIS EYES WERE ON THE CROWD *BEHIND* THE MELCHESTER DUG-OUT . . .

UP THERE...SITTING IN HER *FAVOURITE* SEAT! *GOOD GRIEF,* IT LOOKS LIKE *PENNY...*

...IT *IS* PENNY!

PENNY'S HANDS WERE CLASPED IN A LITTLE SALUTE WHICH MEANT ONLY ONE THING TO ROY . . .

SHE...SHE'S TELLING ME TO STAY *SHARP!* RIGHT TO THE END OF THE GAME!

ER, WHO IS, BOSS?

THE *WIFE!* SHE'S *COME HOME,* PACO!

SO WHY WE WAIT? LET'S GIVE HER SOMETHING TO COME HOME FOR!

FROM PACO DIAZ, THE BALL WAS WORKED OUT TO MERVYN WALLACE . . .

WHAT A RUN! MERV'S GIVEN THE ROVERS A BIT OF *WIDTH!*

THIS IS THE WAY TO *OPEN UP* ZALMO'S BLANKET DEFENCE!

...BUT *THAT* ISN'T! AN OLD-FASHIONED LONG BALL, PUMPED INTO THE GOALMOUTH!

IT'S A *GIFT* FOR ZALMO!

SURE ENOUGH, ZALMO'S MAN-FOR-MAN MARKING SEEMED TO BLOT OUT THE DANGER...

THEIR SWEEPER HAS HEADED IT CLEAR!

PICK UP THAT BALL, MELCHESTER!

YOURS, RACEY...

THE ROCKET!

IT'S IN!

NICE ONE, ROY! THAT TOOK COURAGE TO EVEN HAVE A GO...

...BUT IT CAME OFF!

WAHOOOOOO!

FROM THEN ON, ONLY BRILLIANT DEFENDING BY ZALMO KEPT OUT THE ROVERS, AT HALF-TIME...

LOOK AT ROY! I'VE NEVER SEEN HIM SO ANXIOUS TO GET BACK TO THE DRESSING-ROOM!

IT'S NOT THE DRESSING-ROOM HE'S HEADING FOR, LADDIE!

DUNCAN McKAY WAS RIGHT...

PENNY!

HI, RACEY! YOU'VE STILL GOT A USEFUL LEFT FOOT, I SEE!

BUT DON'T GET ME WRONG, ROY! THIS DOESN'T MEAN THAT I'VE CHANGED MY MIND ABOUT THE AMOUNT OF TIME YOU WERE SPENDING AT THE CLUB!

SO...SO WHY HAVE YOU COME BACK?

WE'LL TALK ABOUT THAT LATER.... AFTER YOU'VE DEALT WITH ZALMO! I DIDN'T COME ALL THE WAY FROM CRETE TO SEE YOU GET KNOCKED OUT OF THE EUROPEAN CUP!

WHAT DO YOU THINK, LADS?

I'M THINKING ABOUT THE FIFTH ROUND, BOSS!

AS THE SECOND-HALF WORE ON, ZALMO'S DETERMINATION TO CLING TO THEIR 3-1 LEAD BECAME MORE AND MORE DESPERATE!

AAAAAAGH!

GOOD GRIEF! THEY ALMOST DRAGGED ROY OFF THE BALL!

DIRECT FREE-KICK TO MELCHESTER!

...AND RACEY'S GOING TO TAKE IT!

IF HE CAN BEAT THAT 'WALL', THIS COULD BE AS GOOD AS A PENALTY!

CAN MELCHESTER OVERCOME THEIR UPHILL TASK? FIND OUT NEXT WEEK!

My marks out of ten for this story:

ROY'S WIFE, PENNY, HAD FLOWN OFF TO CRETE WITH THE RACE TWINS, IN PROTEST AT THE AMOUNT OF TIME HE WAS SPENDING WITH RELEGATION-HAUNTED MELCHESTER ROVERS. BUT SHE HAD RETURNED UNEXPECTEDLY DURING ROVERS' FOURTH ROUND EUROPEAN CUP MATCH AGAINST ZALMO, WHICH THE SWEDISH CHAMPIONS WERE WINNING, 3-1, ON AGGREGATE SCORES. THEN ROVERS WERE AWARDED A DIRECT FREE-KICK...

HIT IT, RACEY! GIVE THEM THE ROCKET!

STAND FAST, ZALMO! HE'S GOING FOR GOAL!

BUT, AT THE LAST SECOND!

ROY'S FLICKED IT SIDEWAYS ...TO BLACKIE GRAY!

WHAT'S THE GOOD OF THAT? THE ZALMO DEFENDERS ARE CLOSING HIM DOWN!

YOU MEAN... I'M DRAWING THEM OUT OF POSITION!

YOURS, JIMMY SLADE!

OH, NO!

AND...

GOOOOAAAAAL!

OHH, WHAT A BRILLIANTLY-WORKED FREE-KICK!

THAT'S PUT US RIGHT BACK INTO THE GAME!

AS THE NOW RAMPANT ROVERS CONTINUED TO CHANGE THEIR TACTICS...

FIRST TIME, RACEY...

A DUNCAN MCKAY SPECIAL! HE'S FOUND ROY WITH THAT LONG THROW!

EEEEAAAAHHH! HOW DID THEIR 'KEEPER GET TO THAT?

CORNER TO MELCHESTER!

UP YOU COME, VIC GUTHRIE!

WATCH HIM, ZALMO! THEY INTEND TO USE GUTHRIE AS A TARGET MAN!

ROY OF THE ROVERS

MELCHESTER ROVERS

ROY'S WIFE, PENNY, HAD FLOWN OFF TO CRETE WITH THE RACE TWINS IN PROTEST AT THE AMOUNT OF TIME HE WAS SPENDING WITH RELEGATION-HAUNTED MELCHESTER ROVERS. HER RETURN CAME TOO LATE TO SAVE ROVERS FROM BEING UNLUCKILY KNOCKED OUT OF THE EUROPEAN CUP... BUT ROY CELEBRATED BY TAKING HIS FAMILY FOR A MEAL IN THE LUXURIOUS RESTAURANT LOUNGE AT MELCHESTER STADIUM...

THIS IS THE LIFE, PENNY! T-BONE STEAK AND A MAGNIFICENT VIEW OF THE GAME!

YOU CAN SAY *THAT* AGAIN, RACEY!

THE MATCH INVOLVED ONE OF THE MELCHESTER JUNIOR TEAMS, IN THE ENGLISH SCHOOLS SHIELD COMPETITION...

MAYBE *YOUNG* ROY WILL BE PLAYING DOWN THERE ONE DAY!

GOOOAA-AAAL!

...THAT'S PUT THEM IN THE SEMI-FINALS! GREAT GOAL BY YOUNG THOMPSON! I'LL HAVE TO KEEP AN EYE ON HIM!

AND THE OTHER EYE ON *YOU*, MY LASS! YOU STILL HAVEN'T TOLD ME WHY YOU CAME BACK!

I HAD A TELEPHONE CALL FROM BLACKIE! MY HEART JUST MELTED WHEN HE TOLD ME THAT YOU WERE RUNNING OUT OF CLEAN SHIRTS AND SOCKS...

...I ALSO REALISED THAT A FOOTBALL MANAGER NEEDS A WIFE WHO STANDS BY HIM DURING THE *BAD* DURING THE *BAD* TIMES, AS WELL AS THE GOOD! SO FROM NOW ON ROY, THERE'LL BE NO MORE COMPLAINTS...

...AS LONG AS YOU TAKE THE TWINS AND I TO CRETE FOR A MID-SEASON BREAK... EVERY YEAR! PROMISE?

PROMISE! IF CLOUGHIE CAN DO IT, SO CAN I!

THAT EVENING, PENNY EMBARKED ON THE TASK OF SHARING ROY'S PROBLEMS...

...IF THE ROVERS GET RELEGATED, I'LL EAT YOUR LEFT BOOT!

STUDS AND ALL? IT'S NO JOKE, WOMAN! IF WE DON'T BEAT REDSTOKE ON SATURDAY, WE'LL HAVE ONE FOOT IN THE SECOND DIVISION!

ROY OF THE ROVERS

MELCHESTER ROVERS

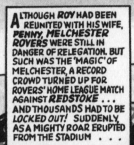

ALTHOUGH *ROY* HAD BEEN REUNITED WITH HIS WIFE, *PENNY, MELCHESTER ROVERS* WERE STILL IN DANGER OF RELEGATION. BUT SUCH WAS THE 'MAGIC' OF MELCHESTER, A RECORD CROWD TURNED UP FOR ROVERS' HOME LEAGUE MATCH AGAINST *REDSTOKE* ... AND THOUSANDS HAD TO BE *LOCKED OUT!* SUDDENLY, AS A MIGHTY ROAR ERUPTED FROM THE STADIUM ...

HURAAAAAAAAAY!

IT'S A GOAL... IT *MUST* BE!

WE'VE TAKEN THE LEAD!

YIPPEEEEE!

BUT THE FANS OUTSIDE WERE WRONG! FOLLOWING A FRANTIC SCRAMBLE IN THE REDSTOKE GOALMOUTH...

...IT'S A PENALTY FOR HANDBALL!

DUNCAN McKAY'S GOING TO TAKE IT!

...THUNDERBOLT!

SAY 'HELLO' TO THE BACK OF THE NET, BALL!

BUT!

AAAAAAAHHHH!

NO GOAL, I'M AFRAID! THEIR 'KEEPER HAS JUST MADE A *FANTASTIC* SAVE!

OH, NO!

NEVER MIND! THERE'S STILL PLENTY OF TIME! SO LET'S DO SOME *CHEERING* OURSELVES!

AYE! SHOUT OUR HEADS OFF FOR THE ROVERS...EVEN THOUGH WE CAN'T SEE THE GAME!

FROM THE AIR, IT WAS AN INCREDIBLE SIGHT...

ROVERS! ROVERS!

MEL-CHES-TER! MEL-CHES-TER!

COME ON, YOU REH-EHHHHDS!

...AT TIMES, THE FANS *OUTSIDE* THE GROUND SHOUTED EVEN LOUDER THAN THE LUCKY ONES!

IN THE FACE OF SUCH AN EAR-SPLITTING DEMONSTRATION OF LOYALTY, THE REDSTOKE DEFENCE WILTED!

OO-OOOOPS!

MIS-KICK... STRAIGHT TO *RACEY!*

HE'S GOT A CHANCE...

NEXT WEEK: A DRESSING-ROOM DISAGREEMENT OVER TACTICS!

ROY OF THE ROVERS

MELCHESTER ROVERS

MELCHESTER PUT TOGETHER A MOVE OF SHEER MAGIC!

WITH MELCHESTER ROVERS IN DANGER OF RELEGATION, ROY WAS UNDER THE GREATEST PRESSURE OF HIS MANAGERIAL CAREER. COULD THE 'REDS' ESCAPE THE DROP, AND PROGRESS BEYOND THE FIFTH ROUND OF THE F.A. CUP? A LOT OF MELCHESTER SUPPORTERS THOUGHT THEY COULD... AS THE ROVERS FOUND OUT AS THEY CAME OUT FOR THE CUP GAME!

MELCHESTER! MELCHESTERRRRR!

ROVERS!

KELBURN!

COME ON, LADS! LET'S SHOW THEM OUR APPRECIATION...

GOOD GRIEF, IT'S LIKE PLAYING AT HOME! OUR FANS ARE DROWNING THE CHANTS OF THE KELBURN PEOPLE!

AS ROY AND HIS PLAYERS LINED UP TO SALUTE THEIR FANS!

WE ALL AGREE... MELCHESTER ROVERS ARE MAGIC!

PEOPLE LIKE THIS MAKE YOU BELIEVE THAT ANYTHING IS POSSIBLE! THEY DESERVE SUCCESS!

AND ROY WAS DETERMINED TO GIVE IT TO THEM. AT THE KICK-OFF...

GREAT INTERCEPTION! RACEY READ THAT PASS PERFECTLY!

CLOSE HIM DOWN, KELBURN...

...TOO LATE! HE'S FOUND VERNON ELIOT!

SHOW THEM YOUR HEELS, VERN!

BUT THE WEST INDIAN WINGER HELD THE BALL... AS JIMMY SLADE POWERED FORWARD!

AWAY YOU GO, MAN!

A BREAK FROM MIDFIELD...

...AND HERE COMES RACE!

SLADE IS LOOKING FOR HIM AT THE NEAR POST...

AS THE KELBURN DEFENCE VEERED TO COVER ROY...

IT'S THERE! RACE LET THE BALL RUN ON ACROSS THE GOAL...

...AND BLACKIE'S KNOCKED IT IN!

HURAAA-AAAAAY!

"COULD THIS BE THE BLACKEST SEASON IN MELCHESTER'S HISTORY?"

ROY OF THE ROVERS

MELCHESTER ROVERS

ROY TRIED DESPERATELY TO SET AN EXAMPLE...

ALTHOUGH *MELCHESTER ROVERS* WERE IN DANGER OF RELEGATION, THOUSANDS OF FANS FOLLOWED THEM TO *KELBURN*, FOR THE FIFTH ROUND OF THE *F.A. CUP.* AFTER BLACKIE GRAY HAD GIVEN THEM THE LEAD, ROVERS DECIDED TO 'SIT' ON THEIR ONE-GOAL ADVANTAGE... AND *ROY'S* WORST FEARS CAME TRUE WHEN KELBURN EQUALISED WITH AN INCREDIBLY LUCKY GOAL!

DON'T SAY I DIDN'T WARN YOU!

PLAYING ON THE RETREAT LEAVES US WIDE OPEN TO FLUKES LIKE THIS!

HE'S RIGHT, LADS! WE'VE GOT TO COME OUT NOW!

SOME OF THE ROVERS WEREN'T CONVINCED, ESPECIALLY VIC GUTHRIE...

THERE'S ONLY A FEW MINUTES LEFT... AND THEY'LL NEVER SCORE *TWO* GOALS LIKE THAT IN ONE GAME! LET'S HANG ON FOR THE REPLAY AND FINISH THEM IN MELCHESTER!

I, ER... DON'T KNOW, VIC...

ROY TRIED DESPERATELY TO SET AN EXAMPLE...

NNNNNF!

WHAT A RUN!

BUT HE'S STILL OUT-NUMBERED!

SOMEHOW, ROY MANAGED TO GET A SHOT IN...

OOOOHHH! CLOSE, ROY ...BUT THAT'S THE WAY TO DO IT!

LET'S HOPE THE REST OF THEM TAKE THE HINT!

BUT, THEN!

AN *UP-AND-UNDER!* THE KELBURN 'KEEPER HAS WHACKED IT RIGHT DOWN THE PARK!

CHAAAAARGE!

LEAVE THE BALL TO CHARLIE CARTER, MELCHESTER!

THAT'S GOOD ADVICE FROM 'GRANDAD' GOSDEN! THE KELBURN PLAYERS WON'T GET NEAR IT!

BUT MERVYN WALLACE WANTED TO MAKE SURE!

MINNNNE!

THE CRAZY IDIOT! HE'S SLICED IT STRAIGHT TO THE FEET OF A KELBURN PLAYER!

NEXT WEEK: THE MOST CRUCIAL MATCH IN MELCHESTER'S HISTORY!

My marks out of ten for this story:

MELCHESTER ROVERS

"IT'LL PUT TREMENDOUS PRESSURE ON US!"

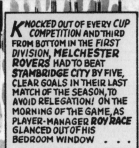

KNOCKED OUT OF EVERY CUP COMPETITION AND THIRD FROM BOTTOM IN THE FIRST DIVISION, MELCHESTER ROVERS HAD TO BEAT STAMBRIDGE CITY BY FIVE, CLEAR GOALS IN THEIR LAST MATCH OF THE SEASON, TO AVOID RELEGATION! ON THE MORNING OF THE GAME, AS PLAYER-MANAGER ROY RACE GLANCED OUT OF HIS BEDROOM WINDOW . . .

THERE HE IS!

GOOD OLD ROY!

THIS IS THE DAY, RACEY!

GOOD GRIEF! THE FANS ARE GATHERING ALREADY . . . OUTSIDE MY HOUSE!

BY THE TIME ROY WAS READY TO LEAVE FOR THE GROUND, POLICE HAD BEEN CALLED IN TO CONTROL THE CROWD . . .

WE COULDN'T GET A TICKET FOR THE MATCH, ROY, SO WE THOUGHT WE'D GIVE YOU A BIG SEND-OFF!

GIVE HIM A KISS, PENNY! SHOW HIM THAT YOU'RE BEHIND HIM, TOO!

THERE . . . THREE KISSES — ONE FOR EVERY GOAL YOU'RE GOING TO SCORE!

HURRAAAAAAY!

HOPE YOU'RE RIGHT, LOVE . . .

ROY DECIDED TO TRAVEL TO THE GROUND IN HIS PRIVATE HELICOPTER, TO AVOID THE CRUSH . . .

WE'LL SUPPORT YOU EVERMORRRRE!

WHAT AN ATMOSPHERE THERE'S GOING TO BE! IT'LL PUT TREMENDOUS PRESSURE ON US!

AND IN THE MELCHESTER DRESSING-ROOM, TWO HOURS LATER . . .

WELL, LADS . . . YOU KNOW WHAT WE'VE GOT TO DO, SO I WON'T WASTE YOUR TIME WITH A TEAM-TALK!

ALL I'LL SAY IS . . . GOOD LUCK . . .

. . . AND STAY SHARP — RIGHT TO THE END OF THE GAME!

THE TEAMS . . . FOR THE MOST CRUCIAL GAME IN THE HISTORY OF MELCHESTER ROVERS!

ROYERS! ROVERS!

CITY! CITY!

MELCHESTER ROVERS	STAMBRIDGE CITY
1 C. CARTER	1 L. COBURN
2 N. BAXTER	2 S. HARRISON
3 D. MC KAY	3 D. BLANDFORD
4 N. GOSDEN	4 R. TAYLOR
5 V. GUTHRIE	5 R. MELLOR
6 J. SLADE	6 T. SANFORD
7 P. DIAZ	7 J. CORRIE
8 B. GRAY	8 P. LONGMAN
9 R. RACE	9 M. REID
10 M. WALLACE	10 J. RICHARDSON
11 V. ELIOT	11 M KENNY
12 A. LYNCH	12 TO BE ANNOUNCED.

ROY OF THE ROVERS

MELCHESTER ROVERS

THE BALL STRUCK THE ANGLE OF THE UPRIGHT AND CROSSBAR!

MELCHESTER ROVERS HAD MADE A BRILLIANT START TO THE MOST CRUCIAL GAME IN THE CLUB'S HISTORY. COMPELLED TO BEAT STAMBRIDGE CITY BY FIVE CLEAR GOALS TO AVOID RELEGATION FROM THE FIRST DIVISION, THEY WERE LEADING 2-0... AS PLAYER-MANAGER ROY RACE UNLEASHED YET ANOTHER SHOT AT CITY'S JITTERY GOALKEEPER...

RACEY'S 'ROCKET'! NUMBER THREE ALL THE WAY!

THE WAY COBURN IS PLAYING, IT'S GOT TO BE!

THE CITY 'KEEPER WAS STILL REACTING AS THE BALL SLAMMED AGAINST HIS SHOULDER...

UU-UUUUGH!

...AND DEFLECTED AGAINST THE ANGLE OF THE UPRIGHT AND CROSSBAR...

...BUT INSTEAD OF BOUNCING DOWN BEHIND THE LINE...

AAAAAHHH! IT'S REBOUNDED STRAIGHT BACK INTO HIS ARMS!

G-GOOD GRIEF!

COBURN SOON RECOVERED FROM HIS INCREDIBLE 'SAVE'!

YOU LUCKY BLIGHTER, COBURN!

YES, THE STROKE OF LUCK HE WAS PRAYING FOR! I'VE A HUNCH HE WON'T BE SO NERVOUS FROM NOW ON!

ROY WAS RIGHT! AS THE ROVERS SWEPT BACK AGAIN...

OOOHHHH! GRANDAD GOSDEN MUST HAVE THOUGHT THAT WAS IN!

HOW DID COBURN GET A HAND TO IT?

FROM THE RESULTING CORNER, PACO DIAZ POWERED IN A VOLLEY...

ANOTHER GREAT SAVE! COBURN'S STOPPING EVERYTHING NOW!

BUT A FEW MINUTES LATER, ROY MADE NO MISTAKE...

GOOOOAAAAL!

IT TOOK A COOL ROY TO BEAT HIM, THOUGH...

MELCHESTER ROVERS 3, STAMBRIDGE CITY 0!

IT REALLY IS A PENALTY NOT TO BE MISSED!

CAN ROVERS STAY IN DIVISION ONE?

ROY OF THE ROVERS

30th MAY, 1981 EVERY MONDAY

15p

THE EYES OF THE FOOTBALL WORLD WERE ON MELCHESTER STADIUM, WHERE THE ROVERS HAD TO BEAT STAMBRIDGE CITY, BY FIVE CLEAR GOALS, IN THEIR LAST MATCH OF THE SEASON, TO AVOID RELEGATION. DESPITE A BRILLIANT DISPLAY BY LEN COBURN, THE CITY 'KEEPER, GOALS FROM ROY, NOEL BAXTER, VIC GUTHRIE AND DUNCAN McKAY HAD GIVEN ROVERS A FOUR—NIL LEAD . . . AND NOW MELCHESTER HAD BEEN AWARDED THEIR SECOND PENALTY!

IT'S ALL UP TO YOU NOW, DUNCAN! THERE'S NO ONE ELSE!

AYE, ROY!

GOOD LUCK, DUNC! KEEP US IN THE FIRST DIVISION!

CONTINUED ON COLOUR PAGES . . .

YOU CAN FIND OUT INSIDE!

©IPC Magazines Ltd., 1981

Australia 45c., New Zealand 45c., Malaysia $1.20.,

ROY OF THE ROVERS

CONTINUED FROM FRONT COVER

SEE FURTHER DEVELOPMENTS SURROUNDING THE FAMOUS ROVERS NEXT WEEK!

ROY OF THE ROVERS

MELCHESTER ROVERS

ROY RACE WAS GOING TO HAVE A 'STAND-IN'!

DESPITE BEING RELEGATED TO THE SECOND DIVISION, MELCHESTER ROVERS' SEASON HAD ENDED WITH AN AMAZING DEMONSTRATION OF LOYALTY FROM THEIR FANS. A TELEVISION PRODUCER WAS SO IMPRESSED, THAT HE PUT AN EQUALLY AMAZING PROPOSITION TO PLAYER-MANAGER ROY RACE . . .

A TELEVISION SERIES... BASED ON THE LIFE AND TIMES OF MELCHESTER ROVERS? I JUST DON'T KNOW! DOES THE CLUB NEED SOMETHING LIKE THIS, ROY?

THAT ALL DEPENDS ON WHAT SIMON BOOKER HAS IN MIND, MISTER CHAIRMAN!

THE TELEVISION PRODUCER SPOKE UP EAGERLY . . .

I'M VISUALISING A SERIES WHICH CAPTURES THE 'MAGIC' OF MELCHESTER ROVERS! THE FANS ... THE PLAYERS ... AND ABOVE ALL, THE TRADITIONS OF A CLUB WHICH IS A WAY OF LIFE TO MANY PEOPLE!

IT CAN DO NOTHING BUT GOOD FOR THE REPUTATION OF FOOTBALL!

WELL, THAT'LL MAKE A CHANGE, ANYWAY!

HEY! SIMON, WHO'S GOING TO PLAY THE PART OF ROY?

THIS IS THE CHAP I'VE GOT IN MIND... ELTON BLAKE!

A LITTLE MAKE-UP AND A WIG, AND IT MIGHT BE HARD TO TELL THE DIFFERENCE!

WEEEOWWW! YOU CAN SAY THAT AGAIN!

AS SIMON BOOKER WENT ON . . .

THE ACTION-SEQUENCES WILL BE VITAL! I WANT TO FILM REAL FOOTBALLERS PLAYING IN COMPETITIVE GAMES, IN FRONT OF GENUINE CROWDS! IT'S THE ONLY WAY TO ACHIEVE REALISM, SAM!

MELCHESTER ROVERS FOOTBA...

I AGREE — BUT YOU CAN'T USE MELCHESTER STADIUM! IT'S BEING RETURFED FOR NEXT SEASON!

WHAT ABOUT THE TOURNAMENT IN SCOTLAND, SAM?

AS ONE OF THE RELEGATED CLUBS, WE'VE BEEN INVITED TO TAKE PART ... ALONG WITH THE THREE TEAMS PROMOTED FROM THE SECOND DIVISION, PLUS THE OUTRIGHT WINNERS OF THE THIRD AND FOURTH DIVISION CHAMPIONSHIPS! SHOULD PROVIDE OLD SIMON WITH ALL THE FILM HE WANTS!

ALTHOUGH RELEGATED TO THE SECOND DIVISION, MELCHESTER ROVERS WERE DETERMINED TO BEGIN THEIR MARCH BACK TO THE TOP BY WINNING A TOURNAMENT IN SCOTLAND. ROY INTENDED GIVING A TRIAL TO KENNY LOGAN, A PROMISING LOCAL PLAYER ... BUT DURING A FULL-SCALE PRACTICE MATCH...

WHICH ONE IS RACE? I'M NOT GOING TO STAND BY WHILE HE FILLS MY SON'S HEAD WITH A LOAD OF DANGEROUS NONSENSE!

UUUUH?

LOOK OUT, ROY ...DON'T SHOOT!

IT WAS TOO LATE!

AAAAAHHHHH!

GOOD GRIEF!

WHERE... WHERE AM I? WHAT HAPPENED?

YOU'VE JUST BEEN HIT BY RACEY'S 'ROCKET', CHUM!

HE SEEMED TO COME OUT OF NOWHERE...

...IT WAS AN ACCIDENT!

NO IT WASN'T! YOU... YOU HIT ME ON HURPOSE! I MEAN, YOU ...PURP ME ON HIP...

I, ER, THINK YOU'D BETTER COME AND LIE DOWN, OLD SON!

GET YOUR HANDS OFF ME, RACE! THIS ONLY CONFIRMS WHAT I'VE ALWAYS SUSPECTED ABOUT FOOTBALL! IT'S A DIRTY ...CYNICAL GAME...

...FIT ONLY FOR HOOLIGANS!

AND YOU'RE ONE OF THEM, RACE! I...I'M GOING TO MAKE SURE YOU DON'T GET YOUR HANDS ON MY KENNY, IF IT'S THE LAST THING I DO!

KENNY?

ROY... I'VE A HUNCH HE WAS TALKING ABOUT KENNY LOGAN!

OH, NO! I'D BETTER GET AFTER HIM!

BE SURE NOT TO MISS WHAT HAPPENS NEXT WEEK!

ROY OF THE ROVERS

MELCHESTER ROVERS

"THE REF ISN'T GOING TO LIKE THAT!"

IN SCOTLAND FOR A TOURNAMENT BETWEEN PROMOTED AND RELEGATED TEAMS, ROY HAD OFFERED A TRIAL TO EIGHTEEN-YEAR-OLD KENNY LOGAN, WHOSE FATHER HATED FOOTBALL, AND WANTED THE LAD TO ENTER THE FAMILY BUSINESS. JUST BEFORE MELCHESTER'S FIRST MATCH, AGAINST WESTON VILLA, LOGAN CAUSED ANOTHER STIR WHEN HE CLASHED WITH TOUGH CENTRE-HALF VIC GUTHRIE...

LOGAN MAY HAVE A BIG MOUTH, BUT LOOK AT HIM GO!

WHAT A RUN!

MOVE THE BALL, LAD! YOU'VE GOT SUPPORT ON BOTH FLANKS!

KEEN TO MAKE AN EARLY IMPRESSION, LOGAN IGNORED THE SHOUTS OF HIS TEAM-MATES...

OO-OOOPS!

HE TRIED TO DO TOO MUCH! THE KID'S LOST IT!

HE NEARLY GOT THROUGH, THOUGH!

NEARLY ISN'T GOOD ENOUGH! NOW WE'VE GOT TO CLEAR UP LOGAN'S MESS!

STEADY, VIC GUTHRIE!

AAAA-OWWW!

HOY, WHAT DO YOU THINK THIS IS, GUTHRIE ... A STREET GAME?

THE REF ISN'T GOING TO LIKE THAT!

THE SPECTATORS WERE RIGHT!

THIS MAY BE A FRIENDLY TOURNAMENT, GUTHRIE, BUT ANY MORE OF THAT AND I'LL BOOK YOU!

GIVE OVER, REF! I HARDLY TOUCHED HIM!

DON'T ARGUE, VIC!

THE RESULTING FREE-KICK TO VILLA BROUGHT THE BEST OUT OF CHARLIE CARTER!

OOOHHHH! ROVERS' MARKING WAS A BIT SLIPSHOD!

GOOD THING 'THE CAT' IS ON FORM!

QUICK ONE, CHARLIE! DON'T HANG ABOUT!

YOUNG LOGAN — DROPPING BACK INTO SPACE! THAT'S WHAT I LIKE TO SEE...

READ NEXT WEEK'S INSTALMENT AND YOU'LL FIND OUT!

My marks out of ten for this story:

ROY OF THE ROVERS

MELCHESTER ROVERS

"I SAID . . . OFF! RIGHT NOW! STEVE NAYLOR IS TAKING YOUR PLACE!"

IN SCOTLAND FOR A TOURNAMENT BETWEEN PROMOTED AND RELEGATED TEAMS, ROY HAD OFFERED A TRIAL TO EIGHTEEN-YEAR-OLD KENNY LOGAN, WHOSE FATHER HATED FOOTBALL, AND WANTED THE LAD TO ENTER THE FAMILY BUSINESS. THEN, DURING MELCHESTER'S FIRST MATCH, AGAINST WESTON VILLA, 'SUPERBRAT' VIC GUTHRIE TOOK A DISLIKE TO THE EXTROVERT LOGAN, AND THE FRICTION BETWEEN THE TWO PLAYERS FORCED ROY TO TAKE DRASTIC ACTION. . . .

...A SUBSTITUTION! LOOKS AS IF RACE HAS DECIDED TO PULL OFF LOGAN... OR COULD IT BE GUTHRIE?

WE'LL SOON FIND OUT!

VIC, I KNOW YOU WON'T UNDERSTAND THIS, BUT I'M ACTING IN THE BEST INTERESTS OF THE TEAM, BELIEVE ME! TAKE A REST, OLD SON!

WHO... ME? NOW, WAIT A MINUTE...

I SAID...OFF! RIGHT NOW! STEVE NAYLOR IS TAKING YOUR PLACE!

BUT—!

THAT'S ENOUGH, VIC! YOU GIVE ME ANY MORE AGGRO AND I'LL SUSPEND YOU FOR THE REST OF THE TOURNAMENT!

AS THE SEETHING MELCHESTER STAR FLOUNCED AWAY...

ROY, I'M NOT TRYING TO TELL YOU HOW TO DO YOUR JOB... BUT THAT SEEMED LIKE A PUBLIC HUMILIATION TO ME!

VIC WAS ASKING FOR IT, BLACKIE! HIS BEHAVIOUR WAS UNSETTLING THE WHOLE TEAM...

...JUST LIKE THE 'SUPERBRAT' OF OLD...

...AND THAT'S SOMETHING I CAN'T AFFORD, WHEN WE'RE TRYING TO RECOVER FROM THE BLOW OF BEING RELEGATED! IT'S VITAL WE WIN THIS TOURNAMENT ... WITH, OR WITHOUT VIC GUTHRIE!

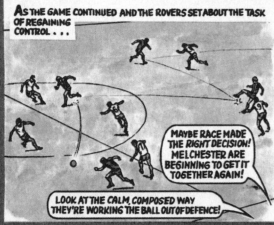

AS THE GAME CONTINUED AND THE ROVERS SET ABOUT THE TASK OF REGAINING CONTROL . . .

MAYBE RACE MADE THE RIGHT DECISION! MELCHESTER ARE BEGINNING TO GET IT TOGETHER AGAIN!

LOOK AT THE CALM, COMPOSED WAY THEY'RE WORKING THE BALL OUT OF DEFENCE!

ROY, ON YOUR LEFT!

KENNY LOGAN'S CALLING FOR IT... BUT HE'S WELL MARKED!

YOU'RE WASTING YOUR BREATH, LAD...

YOU CAN SEE IF IT WORKS OUT NEXT WEEK!

My marks out of ten for this story:

ROY OF THE ROVERS

MELCHESTER ROVERS

AN AMAZING MISKICK; LAUGHTER AND ABUSE . . . ALL IN SIXTY SECONDS!

IN SCOTLAND FOR A TOURNAMENT BETWEEN PROMOTED AND RELEGATED TEAMS, ROY WAS GIVING A TRIAL TO EIGHTEEN-YEAR-OLD KENNY LOGAN, WHOSE FATHER HATED FOOTBALL, AND WANTED THE LAD TO ENTER THE FAMILY BUSINESS. DURING MELCHESTER'S FIRST MATCH, AGAINST WESTON VILLA, ROY WAS FORCED TO PULL OFF 'SUPERBRAT', VIC GUTHRIE, WHO PROMPTLY DISAPPEARED. AS THE SECOND-HALF PROGRESSED, WITH ROVERS LEADING 2-1 . . .

BEAUTIFUL BALL FROM PACO DIAZ... RIGHT ON TO RACE'S FAVOURITE LEFT FOOT!

GIVE IT THE 'ROCKET', ROY!

BUT ROY'S MIND WAS ON OTHER THINGS!

OOOOOPS!

OHHH, WHAT A MIS-KICK!

HE'S SLICED IT STRAIGHT TO KENNY LOGAN!

ALTHOUGH CLOSELY MARKED THE YOUNG SCOT REACTED LIKE LIGHTNING!

HEY! WHAT THE..?

IT'S THERE! AND HE HARDLY HAD ROOM TO MOVE!

FABULOUS GOAL! RIGHT OUT OF NOWHERE!

MELCHESTER ROVERS 3, WESTON VILLA 1!

...AND RACEY MADE IT! FANTASTIC PASS, BOSS!

EVERYONE THOUGHT YE WERE GOING TO TRY A SHOT!

EH..?

EVEN ROY HAD TO GRIN AT LOGAN'S IMPUDENCE!

WHY, YOU CHEEKY LITTLE...

STEADY, ROY! I MEAN, WE ALL THOUGHT IT WAS A GREAT PASS, TOO!

HA, HA! HAAAAAA!

BUT THE ROVERS' LAUGHTER WAS MISUNDERSTOOD BY THE WESTON PLAYERS!

ENJOY THE JOKE, RACE! I HOPE YOU CAN STILL SEE THE FUNNY SIDE OF THINGS NEXT SEASON, WHEN SOME TEAM IS GIVING YOU LOT A THRASHING!

WH-WHAT?

NOW, WAIT A MINUTE... YOU DON'T UNDERSTAND...

IN NEXT WEEK'S INSTALMENT: MEET ROY'S 'STAND-IN'!

ROY SUGGESTED A PEACE MEETING!

IN SCOTLAND FOR A TOURNAMENT BETWEEN PROMOTED AND RELEGATED TEAMS, ROY RACE HAD GIVEN A TRIAL TO EIGHTEEN-YEAR-OLD KENNY LOGAN, WHOSE FATHER HATED FOOTBALL, AND WANTED THE LAD TO ENTER THE FAMILY BUSINESS. AFTER BEATING WESTON VILLA IN THE QUARTER-FINALS, ROY POSED IN A NEW MELCHESTER ROVERS STRIP . . . .

ONE THING'S FOR SURE, LADS... THE ROVERS MAY HAVE BEEN RELEGATED, BUT WE'RE GOING TO BE THE BEST-DRESSED TEAM IN ANY DIVISION, NEXT SEASON!

YOU CAN SAY THAT AGAIN, ROY!

IT'S A GREAT STRIP!

AFTER THE PRESS CONFERENCE, ROY TURNED HIS ATTENTION TO KENNY LOGAN...

WELL, KENNY, I WAS REALLY IMPRESSED BY YOUR PERFORMANCE THIS AFTERNOON! UNDER NORMAL CIRCUMSTANCES, I WOULDN'T HESITATE TO OFFER YOU A CONTRACT...

WHAT DO YOU MEAN, MISTER RACE? WHAT'S THE SNAG?

YOUR FATHER IS THE SNAG! I'VE STILL GOT BAD MEMORIES OF MY FIRST ENCOUNTER WITH HIM...

...IF I SIGN YOU UP WITHOUT EVEN CONSULTING HIM, HE'LL GO BERSERK. SO, I'D LIKE YOU TO TRY AND ARRANGE A SORT OF PEACE MEETING... BETWEEN ALL THREE OF US!

OKAY, MISTER RACE! I'LL DO MY BEST!

LATER, AS KENNY LEFT THE GROUND ON HIS MOTOR BIKE...

SOMEHOW, I FEAR THE WORST! BUT NOW I'D BETTER SEE IF I CAN SORT OUT THE PROBLEM OF VIC GUTHRIE...

HEY, ROY! HAVE YOU GOT A MINUTE?

DENNIS LODER WAS THE DIRECTOR OF THE TELEVISION SERIES WHICH WAS BEING MADE ABOUT THE ROVERS...

I'VE...ER ...GOT A LOT ON MY PLATE, DENNIS...

THIS WON'T TAKE A MINUTE! I WANT YOU TO MEET ONE OF YOUR BIGGEST FANS! HE'S WAITING IN THE CLUB MANAGER'S OFFICE.

AND...

HI, SUPERSTAR!

GREAT SCOTT ALIVE! I—I DON'T BELIEVE IT!

THEN, AS ROY REALISED THAT HE WASN'T STARING AT HIS OWN REFLECTION...

YOU—YOU MUST BE ELTON BLAKE—THE ACTOR WHO'S PLAYING MY PART IN THE TELEVISION SERIES!

THAT'S RIGHT! AMAZING WHAT A WIG AND LITTLE MAKE-UP WILL DO, ISN'T IT?

IN NEXT WEEK'S INSTALMENT: A REBELLION!

ROY OF THE ROVERS

MELCHESTER ROVERS

ROY GOT A 'PHONE CALL FROM KENNY LOGAN'S FATHER!

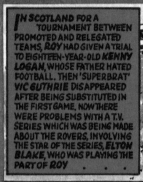

IN SCOTLAND FOR A TOURNAMENT BETWEEN PROMOTED AND RELEGATED TEAMS, ROY HAD GIVEN A TRIAL TO EIGHTEEN-YEAR-OLD KENNY LOGAN, WHOSE FATHER HATED FOOTBALL. THEN 'SUPERBRAT' VIC GUTHRIE DISAPPEARED AFTER BEING SUBSTITUTED IN THE FIRST GAME. NOW THERE WERE PROBLEMS WITH A T.V. SERIES WHICH WAS BEING MADE ABOUT THE ROVERS, INVOLVING THE STAR OF THE SERIES, ELTON BLAKE, WHO WAS PLAYING THE PART OF ROY . . .

JIMMY SLADE'S GOT THE GIGGLES! THE SCENE HAS COLLAPSED INTO A SHAMBLES!

HA! HAA! HAAA!

THE WHOLE SERIES WILL BE A SHAMBLES IF YOU DON'T GET RID OF THESE IDIOTS, LODER...

...THEY'RE RUINING MY CONCENTRATION!

BUT DENNIS LODER, THE DIRECTOR OF THE SERIES, WAS MORE INTERESTED IN A REMARK WHICH HAD BEEN MADE BY ROY'S WIFE . . .

WHAT DID YOU MEAN, PENNY... WHEN YOU SAID THAT ELTON BLAKE DIDN'T LOOK RIGHT FOR THE PART OF ROY?

WELL, JUST LISTEN TO HIM! ROY WOULDN'T DREAM OF TREATING HIS PLAYERS LIKE A BUNCH OF HOOLIGANS...

...AND ANOTHER THING—!

ALL RIGHT, PENNY, YOU'VE SAID YOUR PIECE! LET'S, ER...STICK TO FOOTBALL AND LEAVE TELEVISION TO THE EXPERTS!

SEE YOU LATER, DENNIS!

AS ROY AND PENNY DROVE BACK TO THE HOTEL . . .

...AND IN FUTURE, LASS, KINDLY KEEP YOUR THOUGHTS TO YOURSELF! NO MORE REMARKS ABOUT ELTON BLAKE!

WELL, THAT'S CHARMING! I WAS ONLY TRYING TO PROTECT YOUR IMAGE, ROY RACE!

IF I'M MAKING SUCH A NUISANCE OF MYSELF, MAYBE IT'D BE BETTER FOR EVERYBODY IF I CAUGHT THE NEXT TRAIN HOME... LIKE VIC GUTHRIE!

AWW, DON'T BE LIKE THAT, PENNY...

RECEPTION

AH, JUST IN TIME, MISTER RACE! THERE'S A CALL FOR YOU ON THE RESIDENTS' TELEPHONE!

BUT, I—! OH, ALL RIGHT! I'LL TAKE IT...

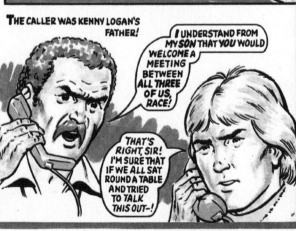

THE CALLER WAS KENNY LOGAN'S FATHER!

I UNDERSTAND FROM MY SON THAT YOU WOULD WELCOME A MEETING BETWEEN ALL THREE OF US, RACE!

THAT'S RIGHT, SIR! I'M SURE THAT IF WE ALL SAT ROUND A TABLE AND TRIED TO TALK THIS OUT—!

NEXT WEEK: A DECISION IS MADE BY BLACKIE GRAY!

BEING RELEGATED FROM THE FIRST DIVISION WAS BAD ENOUGH, BUT NOW ROY HAD RUN INTO MORE PROBLEMS, AS MELCHESTER ROVERS COMPETED IN A SCOTTISH TOURNAMENT FOR PROMOTED AND RELEGATED TEAMS. IN THE SEMI-FINAL, HIS ANXIETIES ABOUT THE FUTURE HAD A TERRIBLE EFFECT ON HIS OWN GAME...

NICE THROW BY CHARLIE CARTER!

NOW LET'S SEE YOU DO SOMETHING WITH THAT, RACE!

HE'S BEEN PLAYING LIKE A GUY WITH TWO LEFT FEET!

ROY'S 'TOUCH' ON THE BALL WAS GOING FROM BAD TO WORSE!

GAAAH! HE'S FUMBLED IT TO ONE OF THEIR MIDFIELD MEN!

OH, N-NO!

FAR POST, IAN...

BEFORE THE MELCHESTER DEFENCE COULD REACT!

GOOAAAAAAAAAL!

ROVERS' OPPONENTS, BLACKTON WANDERERS, HAD JUST BEEN PROMOTED FROM THE THIRD DIVISION...

WE'RE CERTAIN OF FOUR POINTS FROM 'MIGHTY' MELCHESTER, NEXT SEASON!

TOO RIGHT! ROVERS ARE A ONE-MAN TEAM!

WHEN RACE ISN'T ON SONG, THEY'RE USELESS!

AS BLACKTON WENT HUNTING FOR ANOTHER GOAL...

RACE FELL BACK TO HELP OUT HIS DEFENCE... BUT THEY'VE LEFT HIM!

AAAHHH!

MAKE IT TWO-NIL, BLACKTON!

THEN...

NO WAY, MAN!

VERNON ELIOT! THAT'S WHAT YOU CALL PUTTING YOURSELF ABOUT!

HE'S COME FROM OUT ON THE WING TO THE LEFT-BACK POSITION!

ANOTHER MELCHESTER 'OLD HAND' EASED INTO THE ACTION...

WHEN YOU LIKE, VERNON!

THANKS, BLACKIE! COMING OVER!

SEE WHAT HAPPENS IN NEXT WEEK'S INTRIGUING EPISODE!

My marks out of ten for this story:

ROY OF THE ROVERS

MELCHESTER ROVERS

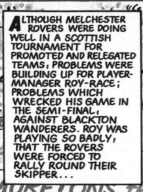

ALTHOUGH MELCHESTER ROVERS WERE DOING WELL IN A SCOTTISH TOURNAMENT FOR PROMOTED AND RELEGATED TEAMS, PROBLEMS WERE BUILDING UP FOR PLAYER-MANAGER ROY-RACE; PROBLEMS WHICH WRECKED HIS GAME IN THE SEMI-FINAL, AGAINST BLACKTON WANDERERS. ROY WAS PLAYING SO BADLY, THAT THE ROVERS WERE FORCED TO RALLY ROUND THEIR SKIPPER...

RACE IS REALLY GETTING THE JITTERS NOW! RATHER THAN TAKE ON THOSE DEFENDERS, HE'S *BACK-HEELED* THE BALL!

WITHOUT EVEN LOOKING ROUND!

THAT'S BECAUSE I *KNEW* SOMEONE WOULD BE THERE— SUPPORTING ME!

BLACKIE GRAY!

KEEP GOING, ROY...

AS ROY DARTED ON...

A *PERFECT* ONE-TWO! ROY'S GOT A CHANCE!

COME OUT FOR IT, 'KEEPER!

TOO LATE!

THREE-ONE TO MELCHESTER! ONE OF THE NEATEST GOALS I EVER SAW!

THE ROVERS ARE REALLY LOOKING AFTER RACEY!

ROY OBLIGED... A MOMENT LATER...IN TYPICAL EXPLOSIVE STYLE...

IF MELCHESTER PLAY LIKE THIS IN THE FINAL, THEY MIGHT AS WELL GIVE THEM THE CUP NOW!

THE 'ROCKET'! RACEY'S BACK IN BUSINESS!

FEELING BETTER, BOSS?

YES, THANKS! BUT I THINK YOU GUYS HAVE MOLLY-CODDLED ME LONG ENOUGH!

RIGHT! IT'S TIME YOU SHOWED THE BLACKTON FANS THAT YOU CAN DO IT ON YOUR OWN!

BUT, AT FULL-TIME AS THE PLAYERS CAME OFF...

ELTON BLAKE... THE BIG-HEADED STAR OF THE TELE-VISION SERIES, WHICH IS BEING MADE ABOUT THE ROVERS!

RIGHT, MISTER RACE, I WANT A *WORD* WITH YOU!

FIND OUT WHAT HAPPENS TO OUR WORRIED HERO NEXT WEEK!

ROY OF THE ROVERS

MELCHESTER ROVERS

ROY'S RELAXED GAME OF GOLF WAS SHATTERED BY RAMPAGING FANS!

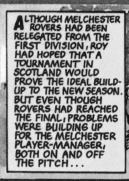

ALTHOUGH MELCHESTER ROVERS HAD BEEN RELEGATED FROM THE FIRST DIVISION, ROY HAD HOPED THAT A TOURNAMENT IN SCOTLAND WOULD PROVE THE IDEAL BUILD-UP TO THE NEW SEASON. BUT EVEN THOUGH ROVERS HAD REACHED THE FINAL, PROBLEMS WERE BUILDING UP FOR THE MELCHESTER PLAYER-MANAGER, BOTH ON AND OFF THE PITCH...

OHHH, *GREAT* SHOT, RACEY! STRAIGHT DOWN THE MIDDLE!

BEST DRIVE I'VE HIT ALL DAY!

PARTNERED BY HIS WIFE, PENNY, ROY WAS PLAYING AGAINST BLACKIE GRAY AND *HIS* WIFE IN A FRIENDLY FOURSOME...

FEELING BETTER, ROY?

YOU BET, BLACKIE! THERE'S NOTHING LIKE A *QUIET* GAME OF GOLF TO RELAX THE MIND! WE'RE *REALLY* AWAY FROM IT ALL OUT HERE!

BUT EVEN AS ROY SPOKE...

THERE THEY ARE! WAHOOOOO!

I *TOLD* YOU I'D TRACK THEM DOWN! GOOD OLD ROY!

WHAT THE—? LOOKS LIKE SOME OF OUR OWN FANS, RAMPAGING ACROSS THE COURSE!

GO ON, ROY! USE SOME MELCHESTER MAGIC TO PUT *THAT* IN THE HOLE!

HA! HAAAAA!

NOW, LOOK HERE, BRINSDEN...

AWW, WHAT'S THE USE! THERE'S NO POINT ARGUING WITH *THIS* LOT!

LET'S HAVE THAT BALL, BLACKIE!

...THIS OUGHT TO GET RID OF THEM!

Roy Race

WHO WANTS MY AUTOGRAPH?

FANTASTIC! THAT'S *MINE!*

LET'S GO!

AS THE MOB OF FANS GALLOPED OFF AFTER THE BALL...

YOU SEEMED TO KNOW THEIR RINGLEADER, ROY!

TREVOR BRINSDEN? AYE, BLACKIE! HE HAD A ROW WITH THE OFFICIAL SUPPORTERS CLUB AND HE'S TRYING TO FORM HIS OWN, BREAKAWAY GROUP...

...SO FAR, HE HASN'T GATHERED MANY PEOPLE AROUND HIM AND I'VE HAD NO REPORTS OF SERIOUS TROUBLE! I...I'D SAY BRINSDEN AND HIS PALS ARE MORE *HIGH-SPIRITED,* THAN INTENTIONAL TROUBLE-MAKERS!

BACK AT THE CLUBHOUSE, ROY WAS CONFRONTED BY THE SECRETARY...

I HAD NO IDEA THEY WERE FOLLOWING ME! I HOPE IT WON'T HAPPEN AGAIN!

I HOPE SO, TOO, MISTER RACE! WE'VE HAD SO MANY COMPLAINTS FROM THE MEMBERS, I AM AFRAID I MUST ASK YOU TO PLAY YOUR GOLF *SOMEWHERE ELSE,* IN FUTURE!

ER, WHAT WAS THAT YOU SAID ABOUT BRINSDEN BEING 'HIGH-SPIRITED', ROY?

ALL RIGHT, BLACKIE; HE'S A *BLOOMING NUISANCE!* NO NEED TO RUB IT IN!

THAT WASN'T THE *LAST* THEY SAW OF TREVOR BRINSDEN AND HIS PALS...

...LOOK AT THEM HANGING AROUND OUTSIDE THE *PARKSIDE* HOTEL! ISN'T THAT WHERE THE *HIGHBORO'* PLAYERS ARE STAYING, ROY?

I HOPE NOT! BRINSDEN'S MOB HAVE CAUSED ENOUGH BOTHER FOR ONE DAY...

HIGHBORO'—ROVERS' OPPONENTS IN THE TOURNAMENT FINAL—HAD BEEN PROMOTED TO THE FIRST DIVISION, THE PREVIOUS SEASON...

ROUND UP THE LADS, BLACKIE! I WANT TO MAKE SURE THEY REALISE JUST HOW IMPORTANT THIS GAME IS FOR US!

ON MY WAY, ROY...

SOON... ...IF WE BEAT HIGHBORO', IT'LL BE ADDITIONAL PROOF THAT MELCHESTER'S RIGHTFUL PLACE IS IN THE *FIRST DIVISION,* SO I WANT YOU ALL TO TURN IN EARLY...

...IT'S *VITAL* THAT WE GET A GOOD NIGHT'S SLEEP!

BUT, JUST AFTER MIDNIGHT... UUU-UUHH! GOOD GRIEF! SOMEONE'S KICKING UP A RACKET, RIGHT OUTSIDE OUR HOTEL!

YOU'VE *NO* CHANCE, MELCHESTER! BOOOO!

HIGHBORO'! HIGHBORO'!

HIGHBORO' FANS...TRYING TO KEEP US AWAKE! BUT *WHY?* THEY'VE A REPUTATION FOR *GOOD BEHAVIOUR...* ONE OF THE BEST IN THE COUNTRY!

WE'RE GOING TO WIN THE CUP! WE'RE GOING TO WIN THE CUP!

DON'T MISS NEXT WEEK'S TENSE AND INCIDENT-PACKED EPISODE!

My marks out of ten for this story:

ROY OF THE ROVERS

MELCHESTER ROVERS

ALTHOUGH *MELCHESTER ROVERS* HAD BEEN RELEGATED FROM THE *FIRST DIVISION*, ROY WAS HOPING FOR A CONVINCING VICTORY OVER *HIGHBORO'* (NEWLY PROMOTED FROM THE *SECOND DIVISION*) IN THE FINAL OF A SCOTTISH TOURNAMENT. BUT ON THE NIGHT BEFORE THE VITAL GAME, THE ROVERS' HOTEL WAS INVADED BY *HIGHBORO'* FANS!

HIGHBORO'! HIGHBORO'!

HEY! LEAVE IT OFF! HOW ARE MY PLAYERS SUPPOSED TO GET A DECENT NIGHT'S SLEEP WITH ALL *THAT* RACKET GOING ON?

GO AND MAKE A NUISANCE OF YOURSELVES OUTSIDE *YOUR* OWN TEAM'S HOTEL!

NO NEED TO, RACE! SOMEONE'S ALREADY DOING IT FOR US . . .

. . . YOUR SUPPORTERS! THERE'S A BUNCH OF THEM DOWN THERE NOW, KEEPING *OUR* PLAYERS AWAKE!

SO WE THOUGHT WE'D HAND OUT THE *SAME* TREATMENT TO THE *ROVERS!*

HIGHBORO'! HIGHBORO'!

ROY HASTILY THREW ON SOME CLOTHES . . .

DO YOU WANT *ME* TO COME ALONG, ROY . . . JUST IN CASE THERE'S ANY *TROUBLE?*

IT MIGHT BE AS WELL, BLACKIE . . .

. . . BUT I'VE A GOOD IDEA WHO'S *BEHIND* ALL THIS . . .

SHORTLY . . .

MELCHESTER! ♪ MELCHESTER!

I THOUGHT SO! IT'S *TREVOR BRINSDEN* AND HIS PALS . . .

PARKSIDE

BRINSDEN'S FANATICAL SUPPORT FOR THE ROVERS HAD ALREADY RESULTED IN ROY BEING BANNED FROM A LOCAL GOLF COURSE . . .

YAHAAAAY! GOOD OLD *ROY!*

WE'RE DOING OUR BIT TO MAKE SURE THE ROVERS *WIN,* TOMORROW!

YOU CRAZY IDIOT, BRINSDEN! WE WANT TO WIN BECAUSE WE'RE THE *BETTER* TEAM, *NOT* BECAUSE THE OPPOSITION ARE *TIRED* OUT!

BUT, ROY! I—!

THE POLICE! LET'S GET OUT OF HERE!

WILL ROY TAKE ADVANTAGE OF THE FANS' MISBEHAVIOUR? SEE NEXT WEEK!

My marks out of ten for this story:

ROY OF THE ROVERS

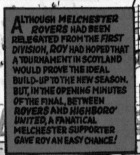

ALTHOUGH MELCHESTER ROVERS HAD BEEN RELEGATED FROM THE FIRST DIVISION, ROY HAD HOPED THAT A TOURNAMENT IN SCOTLAND WOULD PROVE THE IDEAL BUILD-UP TO THE NEW SEASON. BUT, IN THE OPENING MINUTES OF THE FINAL, BETWEEN ROVERS AND HIGHBORO' UNITED, A FANATICAL MELCHESTER SUPPORTER GAVE ROY AN EASY CHANCE!

THOSE STREAMERS HAVE UNSETTLED THE HIGHBORO' 'KEEPER! ROY HAS ONLY GOT TO KNOCK IT PAST HIM AND ROVERS ARE ONE UP!

HIGHBORO

BUT, INCREDIBLY!

HECK, HE'S STUCK IT OVER THE BAR... FROM ONLY TEN YARDS!

WHAT HAPPENED TO THE FAMOUS 'ROCKET', RACE?

I'VE A HUNCH YOU HELD IT BACK, RACEY! YOU MISSED THAT GOAL DELIBERATELY!

DEAD RIGHT, BLACKIE...

... I REFUSE TO TAKE ADVANTAGE OF THE CRAZY BEHAVIOUR OF OUR SO-CALLED 'FANS'! NO TEAM CAN TAKE PRIDE IN SCORING A GOAL THAT HASN'T BEEN CREATED WITHIN THE RULES OF THE GAME!

REF..., PERMISSION TO LEAVE THE FIELD FOR A MOMENT? I THINK I CAN PUT A STOP TO THAT NONSENSE BEHIND THE HIGHBORO' GOAL!

BE MY GUEST, ROY...

GOLA

ROY SOUGHT OUT ONE OF THE POLICEMEN ON DUTY IN THE STADIUM...

OFFICER, I THINK I KNOW THE CHAP WHO'S BEEN TRYING TO TURN THIS MATCH INTO A CARNIVAL! IF I GIVE YOU HIS NAME AND DESCRIPTION...

BORO

WE'LL KEEP A CLOSE EYE ON HIM FROM NOW ON! FIRE AWAY, ROY...

THE GAME HAD CONTINUED IN ROY'S ABSENCE ...AND SOON...

'BORO' ARE REALLY TAKING ADVANTAGE OF THE FACT THAT ROVERS ARE DOWN TO TEN MEN!

AFTER BEING KEPT AWAKE MOST OF THE NIGHT BY THOSE MELCHESTER FANS, I DON'T BLAME THEM!

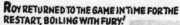

IN NEXT WEEK'S INSTALMENT: THE "ROCKET" RULES!

ROY OF THE ROVERS

EVEN ROY WAS FEELING THE BLISTERING PACE OF THE GAME!

ALTHOUGH MELCHESTER ROVERS HAD BEEN RELEGATED FROM THE FIRST DIVISION, ROY HAD HOPED THAT A TOURNAMENT IN SCOTLAND WOULD PROVE THE IDEAL BUILD-UP TO THE NEW SEASON. BUT HE FOUND HIMSELF MAKING A NUMBER OF ENEMIES AND WAS FORCED TO REPORT TREVOR BRINSDEN—A FANATICAL MELCHESTER FAN—TO THE POLICE, DURING THE TOURNAMENT FINAL AGAINST HIGHBORO' UNITED . . .

MEL-CHES-TER RO-VERS... MELCHESTER RO-VERS... I'LL SUPPORT YOU EVERMORE ♪ EVERMORRRRRRE! ♫

STREAMERS ARE FOR PARTIES, LAD, NOT FOOTBALL MATCHES!

LET'S GO!

ROY SOUGHT OUT THE CAPTAIN OF HIGHBORO' . . .

THAT'S THE KIND OF SUPPORT WE DON'T WANT, GORDON! SORRY IT HAD TO HAPPEN!

WELL, HE'S GONE NOW, ROY . . .

. . . SO LET'S SETTLE DOWN, AND MAKE A GAME OF IT, EH?

AND SO . . .

OOOHHHHH! ROY WAS JUST WIDE!

HE HAD A GO, WHEN 'BORO' WERE EXPECTING HIM TO LAY IT OFF!

MOMENTS LATER, AS HIGHBORO' HIT BACK . . .

SAAAAAVED! CHARLIE CARTER!

STILL ONE-ALL!

NEITHER SIDE CAN GET A GRIP ON THE GAME...

EVEN ROY WAS FEELING THE PACE...

YOU WOULDN'T THINK THIS WAS SUPPOSED TO BE A 'FRIENDLY' WOULD YOU, BLACKIE?

THERE'S A LOT AT STAKE, ROY! HIGHBORO' WANT TO PROVE THEY DESERVE TO TAKE OUR PLACE IN THE FIRST DIVISION!

YOU'RE RIGHT! AND WE, IN TURN, WANT TO SHOW THE WORLD THAT THE SECOND DIVISION IS NO PLACE FOR THE ROVERS!

AS ROVERS BEGAN TO DRAW UPON ALL THEIR VAST SKILL AND EXPERIENCE...

LOVELY BREAK BY NOEL BAXTER!

THAT'S THE STUFF, ROVERS! LET'S SHOW THEM WE DIDN'T DESERVE TO BE RELEGATED!

NEXT WEEK: ROVERS' FIRST MATCH IN THE SECOND DIVISION!

My marks out of ten for this story:

© IPC Magazines Ltd., 1981

Australia 45c., New Zealand 45c., Malaysia $1.25., IR 23p (inc VAT)

ROY OF THE ROVERS

CONTINUED FROM FRONT COVER

THE ROVERS POSED FOR A TEAM PHOTOGRAPH...

AS THE PLAYERS BROKE UP FOR THE WARM-UP SESSION...

AFTER THE TROUBLE HE CAUSED IN SCOTLAND, HE CAN CONSIDER HIMSELF LUCKY THAT ROY INCLUDED HIM IN THE SQUAD!

VIC GUTHRIE CAN PUT HIS TRACK-SUIT BACK ON! HE'S SUBSTITUTE TODAY!

GUTHRIE HAD STORMED HOME FROM SCOTLAND IN A TEMPER, AFTER BEING PULLED OUT OF A GAME...

...I STILL SAY THAT ROY SHOULD HAVE SUSPENDED HIM!

IT'S DIFFICULT TO KNOW HOW TO HANDLE THE 'SUPERBRAT!' GIVING HIM ANOTHER CHANCE COULD BE A BIG MISTAKE!

AS THE TEAMS LINED UP...

RIGHT, BARNBURY!

KEEP IT TIGHT AND PLAY IT COOL! LET'S SHOW THEM WE'RE NOT OVERAWED BY MELCHESTER'S REPUTATION!

OKAY, LADS... LET'S START THE CLIMB BACK TO THE FIRST DIVISION AS SOON AS THAT WHISTLE BLOWS!

RIGHT ON!

WE'RE WITH YOU, ROY...

AND...

THEY'RE AWAAAAAAAY!

ROVERS! ♪ ROVERS!

ROY AND BLACKIE GRAY SOON COMBINED TO RELEASE JIMMY SLADE...

THERE GOES THE POWERHOUSE!

ONE OF YOUR SPECIALS! HIT IT ON THE RUN!

NEXT WEEK: VIC GUTHRIE'S AT HIS BEST . . . AND WORST!

ROY OF THE ROVERS

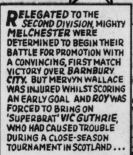

RELEGATED TO THE SECOND DIVISION, MIGHTY MELCHESTER WERE DETERMINED TO BEGIN THEIR BATTLE FOR PROMOTION WITH A CONVINCING, FIRST MATCH VICTORY OVER BARNBURY CITY. BUT MERVYN WALLACE WAS INJURED WHILST SCORING AN EARLY GOAL AND ROY WAS FORCED TO BRING ON 'SUPERBRAT' VIC GUTHRIE, WHO HAD CAUSED TROUBLE DURING A CLOSE-SEASON TOURNAMENT IN SCOTLAND...

VIC, I WANT YOU TO SLOT INTO THE BACK-FOUR...LEFT SIDE OF THE PARK, IN PLACE OF STEVE NAYLOR! I'M PUSHING HIM UP INTO MIDFIELD!

WHY NAYLOR, ROY? I CAN PLAY ANYWHERE! I STARTED IN MIDFIELD!

OH, OH! HE'S OFF ALREADY!

NOW, LOOK-!

OKAY! OKAY! SORRY I SPOKE! BACK-FOUR, IT IS! YOU'RE THE BOSS, ROY!

WELL, AT LEAST GUTHRIE SEEMS TO BE TRYING TO BEHAVE HIMSELF! LET'S JUST HOPE HE KEEPS IT UP!

GUTHRIE WAS SOON IN ACTION...

GREAT CLEARANCE!

WHEN HE CONCENTRATES ON HIS JOB AND KEEPS HIS COOL, VIC'S ONE OF THE MOST RELIABLE DEFENDERS IN THE LEAGUE!

BUT...

HEYYYYY!

OOOPS! A COLLISION BETWEEN VIC AND BRIAN NORTON, THE CITY STRIKER!

THERE'LL BE TROUBLE NOW...

GUTHRIE'S NOTORIOUS TEMPER FLARED...

COME ON, REF! HE DIDN'T EVEN GO FOR THE BALL!

IT WAS AN ACCIDENT, HONEST! I COULDN'T STOP!

ALL RIGHT, THAT'S ENOUGH...

...I'LL ACCEPT IT WAS AN ACCIDENT...THIS TIME! BUT I'M KEEPING AN EYE ON YOU TWO! ANY MORE TROUBLE AND I WON'T BE SO LENIENT!

FAIR ENOUGH, REF...

ROY OF THE ROVERS

DURING MELCHESTER ROVERS' FIRST MATCH IN THE SECOND DIVISION, AGAINST BARNBURY CITY, ROY WAS FORCED TO BRING ON 'SUPERBRAT' VIC GUTHRIE AFTER AN INJURY TO MERVYN WALLACE. A NIGGLING RUNNING BATTLE DEVELOPED BETWEEN GUTHRIE AND A CITY STRIKER . . . AND THEN ROY WAS FACED WITH A GRIM DECISION . . .

WELL, ROY . . . YOU'RE THE ONLY PERSON WHO HAD A CLEAR VIEW OF THE INCIDENT . . . DID GUTHRIE RETALIATE AGAINST NORTON?

I'LL ACCEPT WHATEVER YOU SAY!

I KNOW YOU WILL, REF . . .

. . . AND I'VE GOT TO TELL THE TRUTH! IF I LET MY OWN PLAYERS OFF THE HOOK, HOW CAN I CRITICISE OTHER MANAGERS WHO REFUSE TO PUNISH FOOTBALL THUGGERY?

AND, SO!

GUTHRIE RETALIATED, ALL RIGHT, REF! IT WAS A DELIBERATE PUNCH!

THE REFEREE PROMPTLY BOOKED BRIAN NORTON, THE CITY STRIKER, AND THEN HE DEALT WITH GUTHRIE . . .

HE'S SENDING GUTHRIE OFF!

ROY HAS VIRTUALLY SACRIFICED ONE OF HIS OWN PLAYERS!

GUTHRIE ALMOST CHOKED WITH FURY . . .

THIS PROVES YOU'VE GOT IT IN FOR ME!

SORRY, VIC, BUT YOU WERE ASKING FOR IT . . . . . . NOW GET GOING!

. . . YOU CAN SAY YOUR PIECE AFTER THE GAME . . . IN MY OFFICE!

AS THE SUPERBRAT STORMED OFF . . .

HE'S THROWN HIS SHIRT AT TAFFY MORGAN! WHAT A TERRIBLE ADVERTISEMENT FOR FOOTBALL!

ROY'S REALLY GOT TROUBLE ON HIS HANDS NOW . . .

. . . AND ROVERS ARE DOWN TO TEN MEN!

IF CITY CAN SCORE FROM THE FREE-KICK, THEY'LL BE RIGHT BACK IN THE GAME!

ROY OF THE ROVERS

MELCHESTER ROVERS HAD BEGUN THEIR FIRST SEASON IN THE SECOND DIVISION, WITH A TREMENDOUS 5-0 VICTORY OVER BARNBURY CITY, DESPITE A CHILDISH DISPLAY BY 'SUPERBRAT' VIC GUTHRIE, WHO WAS EVENTUALLY SENT OFF. BUT NOW, ROY, AFTER RECEIVING A TELEPHONE CALL FROM HIS WIFE, WAS DRIVING HOME TO YET ANOTHER PROBLEM!

LOOK AT THE WAY HE'S PARKED HIS CAR! SEEMS MY LOVEABLE, LONG-LOST COUSIN HASN'T CHANGED ONE BIT!

AS ROY HURRIED INDOORS...

ARNIE MECKIFF!

IN THE FLESH, ROY, YOU LITTLE RIPPER! HEY, THIS PRETTY 'SHEILA' OF YOURS CAN SURE LAY ON A SPREAD...

...AND WHAT ABOUT THESE TWO LITTLE BEAUTS! HOW'S YOUR LEFT FOOT, SPORT? GOT A 'ROCKET' IN IT, LIKE YOUR DAD?

DON'T LIKE HIM, DADDY!

NOR DO I, SON...

WHAT DO YOU WANT, ARNIE? JUST PASSING THROUGH... I HOPE!

AWW, COME ON, WONDERMAN! DON'T BE LIKE THAT! ALL I NEED IS A FEW DAYS' LODGINGS...

...UNTIL I FIND MY FEET, AS YOU MIGHT SAY!

THE SPARE ROOM WILL DO FINE! FIRST LEFT AT THE TOP OF THE STAIRS, I THINK YOU SAID, PENNY!

NOW, WAIT A MINUTE, ARNIE...

AS ROY'S COUSIN WENT THUDDING UPSTAIRS...

SORRY, ROY! HE—HE JUST CAME BARGING IN AND MADE HIMSELF AT HOME! IS HE THE DREADED ARNIE THAT YOU'VE MENTIONED IN THE PAST?

UNFORTUNATELY, YES...

...ARNIE EMIGRATED TO AUSTRALIA WITH HIS FAMILY ABOUT FIFTEEN YEARS AGO! WHENEVER HE SHOWS UP, HE'S EITHER IN TROUBLE, OR WANTS TO BORROW MONEY... AND I'VE BEEN WEAK ENOUGH TO OBLIGE HIM! BUT HE'S IN FOR A DISAPPOINTMENT, THIS TIME!

ROY HAD GIVEN 18 YEAR-OLD KENNY LOGAN A TRIAL, DURING A CLOSE-SEASON TOURNAMENT IN SCOTLAND, AND HAD BEEN VASTLY IMPRESSED WITH THE LAD. BUT ROY HAD CLASHED WITH KENNY'S FATHER, WHO WANTED THE BOY TO ENTER THE FAMILY BUSINESS AND WAS BITTERLY OPPOSED TO HIM BECOMING A PROFESSIONAL FOOTBALLER...

NEXT WEEK: ROVERS SERVE UP SOME FANTASTIC FOOTBALL!

My marks out of ten for this story:

ROY OF THE ROVERS

"THERE'S A BIT OF A DISTURBANCE INVOLVING VIC GUTHRIE!"

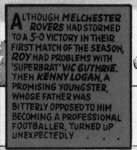

ALTHOUGH MELCHESTER ROVERS HAD STORMED TO A 5-0 VICTORY IN THEIR FIRST MATCH OF THE SEASON, ROY HAD PROBLEMS WITH 'SUPERBRAT' VIC GUTHRIE. THEN KENNY LOGAN, A PROMISING YOUNGSTER, WHOSE FATHER WAS BITTERLY OPPOSED TO HIM BECOMING A PROFESSIONAL FOOTBALLER, TURNED UP UNEXPECTEDLY . . .

YESSSS!

YOUNG LOGAN'S DONE IT AGAIN... HE SNEAKED IN OUT OF NOWHERE!

THAT'S THE MARK OF A BORN STRIKER!

HEAR THAT, ROY? MAYBE I WAS BORN TO PLAY FOR MELCHESTER ROVERS!

CHEEKY LITTLE BLIGHTER!

AYE, BUT THAT'S PART OF HIS IMAGE, TAFF! KENNY WOULDN'T BE SUCH A GOOD PLAYER IF HE DIDN'T HAVE AN IMPISH STREAK!

EVEN SO, ROY... SCORING GOALS IN TOURNAMENTS AND PRACTICE MATCHES IS A BIT DIFFERENT FROM THE REAL THING!

THE SAME THOUGHT HAD ALREADY OCCURRED TO ROY...

...AND APART FROM THAT, I THINK I OUGHT TO HAVE A FINAL CHAT WITH HIS FATHER BEFORE I COME TO ANY DECISION!

SUDDENLY!

ROY, YOU'RE WANTED AT THE MAIN ENTRANCE! THERE'S A BIT OF A DISTURBANCE INVOLVING VIC GUTHRIE!

OH, NO!

SECONDS LATER...

OOOOF!

CLEAR OFF! WHY CAN'T YOU NEWS-HOUNDS LEAVE ME ALONE?

VIC! CUT THAT OUT!

GUTHRIE HAD BEEN SENT OFF DURING ROVERS' FIRST MATCH...

HAVEN'T YOU CAUSED ENOUGH TROUBLE LATELY?

YOU'RE ALL AGAINST ME...

...JUST BECAUSE THE FANS NICKNAMED ME 'SUPERBRAT'! I DEMAND FAIR TREATMENT!

MORE MELCHESTER MAGIC IN NEXT WEEK'S INSTALMENT!

ROY OF THE ROVERS

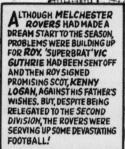

NEXT WEEK: MORE PROBLEMS FOR THE MELCHESTER SUPERSTAR!

My marks out of ten for this story:

ROY OF THE ROVERS

Although relegated to the Second Division, Melchester Rovers had made a brilliant start to the season, but off-the-field problems were building up for Roy. After his villainous cousin, Arnie Meckiff, arrived from Australia unexpectedly, Roy returned from an away game to find that a Melchester shop was under new ownership...

So THIS is Arnie's latest wheeze! He's set himself up as a LAND-AGENT!

BUY A PLOT NOW!

Seaside plots available from only £5,000!

But... only five thousand pounds for a plot of land, overlooking the sea? It's just GOT to be a HOAX!

WHAT HAS, RACEY?

That's what I intend to find out, Blackie! You and the other lads carry on! I'll take this taxi back to my place!

But Roy found another problem waiting on his doorstep!

So THERE you are, RACE!

GOOD GRIEF! IT'S KENNY LOGAN'S FATHER! HE'S FOLLOWED THE LAD DOWN FROM SCOTLAND!

Roy had signed promising young Kenny Logan against the wishes of his father, who wanted the boy to enter the family business...

...YOU WENT BEHIND MY BACK! YOU'VE ENTICED MY SON AWAY FROM ME!

I DIDN'T ENTICE ANYONE! KENNY'S EIGHTEEN! HE'S OLD ENOUGH TO MAKE HIS OWN DECISIONS, MISTER LOGAN!

AND WHAT HAPPENS IF HE DOESN'T COME UP TO YOUR EXPECTATIONS? YOU'LL PROBABLY THROW HIM ON THE SOCCER SCRAP-HEAP!

I DON'T BELIEVE IT! HE'S GOING TO TAKE A PUNCH AT ME.

HEY! TAKE IT EASY!

UU-UNNNNNF!

ARTHUR! STOP IT!

YOU—YOU'RE ONLY MAKING THINGS WORSE FOR KENNY! EVERYONE SAYS THAT HE COULDN'T HAVE SIGNED FOR A BETTER CLUB!

THERE'S NO SUCH THING AS A GOOD FOOTBALL CLUB...

...AND IF THERE'S ANY CHANCE OF BRINGING MY BOY TO HIS SENSES, RACE, I'M GOING TO TAKE IT — NO MATTER WHAT THE COST... TO YOU, OR MELCHESTER ROVERS!

AS THE FUMING FATHER CLIMBED BACK INTO HIS CAR AND DROVE OFF...

THAT SOUNDED LIKE A DANGEROUS THREAT TO ME! MY STARS, DEALING WITH ARNIE MECKIFF IS GOING TO SEEM LIKE A PICNIC AFTER THIS!

BUT, AS ROY SOON DISCOVERED, HIS COUSIN HAD ALREADY PACKED HIS BAGS!

...ANY IDEA WHERE HE'S GONE, PENNY? ANY MESSAGE?

NO, ROY! HE JUST SAID HE'D FOUND A FLAT, OR SOMETHING... AND THAT HE'D BE IN TOUCH!

WELL, IF HE DOESN'T... SOMEONE'S GOING TO GET IN TOUCH WITH HIM! AND I KNOW JUST THE MAN FOR THE JOB!

WHAT DO YOU MEAN, ROY? WHAT ARE YOU GOING TO DO?

ROY KEPT QUIET ABOUT HIS PLANS FOR ARNIE MECKIFF. AS HE ARRIVED AT MELCHESTER STADIUM, THE FOLLOWING DAY...

ROVERS F.C.

HELLO! LOOKS LIKE THE TELEVISION BOYS ARE HERE IN FORCE, TODAY...

TV FILM UNIT

A TELEVISION SERIES, ENTITLED 'THE MAGIC OF MELCHESTER', WAS BEING MADE ABOUT THE ROVERS...

...AND THAT LOOKS LIKE ELTON BLAKE, THE STAR OF THE SERIES! THE CHAP WHO IS PLAYING THE PART OF ME!

Gola

THE PROGRAMME DIRECTOR, DENNIS LODER, WAS WAITING FOR ROY...

...WE'LL ONLY BE FILMING FOR ABOUT HALF-AN-HOUR, ROY! THEN YOU CAN GET ON WITH TRAINING!

THAT'S OKAY, DENNIS! BUT WHAT'S ELTON BLAKE DOING HERE... IN FULL KIT?

HE'S, ER... NOT TURNING OUT TOO WELL IN THE CLOSE-UP ACTION SHOTS, SO I WAS HOPING YOU'D GIVE HIM A BIT OF COACHING... SO THAT HE AT LEAST LOOKS LIKE A FOOTBALLER!

BLAKE HAD ALREADY ACCUSED ROY OF TRYING TO GET HIM SACKED FROM THE SERIES...

AAAO-OWWGH!

...AND NOW I'VE GOT TO TURN HIM INTO A FOOTBALLER! BUT, HE — HE'S HOPELESS! HE CAN'T EVEN KICK A FOOTBALL PROPERLY!

Gola

NEXT WEEK: THERE'S NO END TO ROY'S MOUNTING PROBLEMS!

My marks out of ten for this story:

ROY OF THE ROVERS

ALTHOUGH RELEGATED TO THE SECOND DIVISION, MELCHESTER ROVERS HAD TAKEN MAXIMUM POINTS FROM THEIR EARLY LEAGUE GAMES. BUT OFF-THE-FIELD PROBLEMS WERE BUILDING UP FOR ROY. ONE OF THEM WAS ELTON BLAKE, THE STAR OF A TELEVISION SERIES WHICH WAS BEING MADE ABOUT THE ROVERS, AND ROY HAD BEEN ASKED TO COACH HIM . . .

...SO GET YOUR NON-KICKING FOOT ALONGSIDE THE BALL; BODY LEANING RIGHT FORWARD... ...AND DON'T FORGET TO KEEP YOUR HEAD—!

ALL RIGHT, RACE, I THINK I KNOW HOW TO KICK A FOOTBALL PROPERLY!

OKAY, ELTON... TAKE A SHOT AT CHARLIE CARTER FROM THE PENALTY-SPOT! AIM TO KEEP THE BALL LOW!

PRETTY BASIC STUFF! BUT IF YOU INSIST...

OOOPS!

SEE WHAT I MEAN? YOUR BODY WAS LEANING TOO FAR BACK AT THE MOMENT OF CONTACT!

AS BLAKE TRIED AGAIN...

AAAOWWGH!

YOU OVERDID IT, THAT TIME! YOUR LEFT FOOT WAS PLACED TOO FAR IN FRONT OF THE BALL!

ROY WAS BEGINNING TO DESPAIR OF TEACHING THE CONCEITED ACTOR ANYTHING!

ER, LET'S TRY SOME HEADERS, ELTON! TRY AND GET SLIGHTLY ABOVE THE BALL AT IMPACT... AND USE YOUR NECK MUSCLES!

ALL RIGHT! GET ON WITH IT...

UUULLLLGH!

GOOD GRIEF! HE'S HEADED IT WITH HIS NOSE!

SOME OF THE WATCHING ROVERS COULDN'T RESTRAIN THEMSELVES ANY LONGER!

IF THEY PUT THAT IN THE SHOW, THE VIEWERS WILL THINK IT'S A COMEDY SERIES!

WHY, YOU—!

In fact, Roy had one or two *other* worries!

With Mervyn Wallace also out of action because of injury, Roy had brought in Cyril 'Storky' Knight and had decided to give Kenny Logan his first outing with the seniors. The Melchester team . . .

C. CARTER

N. BAXTER   S. NAYLOR   C. KNIGHT   D. MCKAY

J. SLADE   B. GRAY   P. DIAZ

K. LOGAN   R. RACE   V. ELIOT

SUB: T. CASSIDY

NEXT WEEK: ROY LEAVES THE PITCH AND GOES ON TO THE TERRACES!

My marks out of ten for this story:

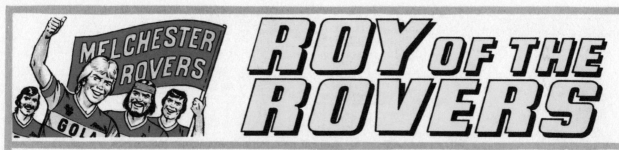

ROY OF THE ROVERS

ROY WAS DISTRACTED AND LOST HIS CONCENTRATION!

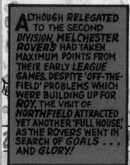

Although relegated to the Second Division, Melchester Rovers had taken maximum points from their early League games, despite 'off-the-field' problems which were building up for Roy. The visit of Northfield attracted yet another 'full house', as the Rovers went in search of goals... and glory!

GREAT TACKLE BY 'STORKY' KNIGHT! HE'S WORKED THE BALL TO ROY!

NNNNNNG!

WHAT'S THE RECORD FOR THE GREATEST NUMBER OF CONSECUTIVE LEAGUE VICTORIES, FROM THE START OF THE SEASON?

ELEVEN, I THINK!

...AND THE ROVERS ARE GOING TO BREAK IT... ESPECIALLY IF THEY KEEP PLAYING LIKE THIS!

BRILLIANT REVERSE BALL TO VERNON ELIOT!

...AND IT'S THERE!

WAHOOOOOO! ROCK ON, YOU ROVERS!

BUT AT THAT MOMENT!

WHY DON'T YOU INVADE THE PITCH, NORTHFIELD? THAT'S THE ONLY WAY YOU'LL SAVE YOUR MOB FROM BEING THRASHED!

WHY, THAT STUPID...

I'M ROY'S GREATEST FAN

FORTUNATELY, MOST OF THE NORTHFIELD FANS REFUSED TO BE PROVOKED...

FORGET IT, LADS! IT'S IDIOTS LIKE HIM WHO GET OTHER PEOPLE INTO TROUBLE!

'THERE'S ONLY ONE ♪ ROY ♪ RACE...'

IGNORE HIM!

'...ONLY ONE ♪ ROYYYY ♪ RAAACE!'

THAT VOICE! IT'S GOT TO BE TREVOR BRINSDEN!

ROY! WATCH THAT BALL!

Brinsden had already caused serious trouble at a tournament in Scotland, and at an away game...

DARN IT! HE'S EVEN MAKING ME LOSE MY CONCENTRATION NOW!

NOW, NOW, ROY! KEEP YOUR MIND ON THE GAME!

WHAT'S ROY ABOUT TO DO? YOU CAN FIND OUT NEXT WEEK!

ROY OF THE ROVERS

ROY'S HANDLING OF HIS 'GREATEST FAN' WAS SENSATIONAL!

ALTHOUGH **RELEGATED** TO THE **SECOND DIVISION**, MELCHESTER **ROVERS** WERE UNBEATEN IN THE **LEAGUE**, DESPITE OFF-THE-FIELD PROBLEMS WHICH WERE BUILDING UP FOR **ROY**. ONE OF THESE PROBLEMS WAS **TREVOR BRINSDEN**, A FANATICAL FAN WHO STIRRED UP TROUBLE IN A HOME MATCH AGAINST **NORTHFIELD**. AND AT HALF-TIME . . .

WAHOOOOO!

LOOK AT ROY — DRAGGING YOUNG BRINSDEN OUT INTO THE MIDDLE OF THE PITCH!

AND BRINSDEN'S LOVING IT!

ROY, I NEVER THOUGHT YOU'D GO TO **THESE** LENGTHS TO INTRODUCE ME AS YOUR **GREATEST FAN!**

YOU'RE A 'FAN' OF MINE, ALL RIGHT, BRINSDEN...

...THE KIND OF FAN I CAN DO WITHOUT! **LISTEN, EVERYBODY!** I WANT YOU TO TAKE A GOOD LOOK AT THIS CHARACTER! HE WAS TRYING TO PROVOKE A BUNCH OF **NORTHFIELD** FANS . . .

UUUUH?

A HUSH FELL OVER MELCHESTER STADIUM AS ROY WENT ON . . .

...FOOTBALL NEEDS ALL THE SUPPORTERS IT CAN GET, THESE DAYS... AND I MEAN SUPPORTERS, NOT **FANATICS!** LOYALTY TO A PARTICULAR CLUB **MUST** BE BLENDED WITH **RESPECT** FOR YOUR OPPONENTS...

...HOTHEADS LIKE BRINSDEN DON'T KNOW THE MEANING OF '**RESPECT**'! HIS KIND ARE A **MENACE** TO FOOTBALL...

ROY, IT'S OLD TREVOR YOU'RE TALKING ABOUT! YOUR **GREATEST FAN!**

...IF HE INSISTS ON BEHAVING LIKE AN **IDIOT**, HE'LL HAVE TO BE TREATED LIKE ONE ... SO I'M **BANNING** HIM FROM MELCHESTER'S HOME GAMES FOR THE **REST** OF THE SEASON!

WH-WHAAAAAT?

OKAY, BOYS...I'VE FINISHED WITH HIM! YOU CAN THROW HIM **OUT** OF THE STADIUM!

NO, PLEASE! NOT FOR THE WHOLE SEASON ...

IN NEXT WEEK'S INSTALMENT: AN ATTEMPT ON ROY'S LIFE!

My marks out of ten for this story:

ROY OF THE ROVERS

14th NOVEMBER, 1981 EVERY MONDAY

16p

©IPC Magazines Ltd., 1981

46c., New Zealand 45c., Malaysia $ 1 25, IR 23p (inc. VAT)

PRESSMEN CLAMOURED FOR ROY'S ATTENTION...

ROY, WHAT'S YOUR REACTION TO THE POSSIBILITY OF BREAKING THE LEAGUE RECORD?

NOT A LOT! NOW, IF YOU'LL EXCUSE ME, LADS...

UUUUH?

WHAT AN ANTI-CLIMAX! ROY SEEMS TO HAVE FORGOTTEN THE MATCH ALREADY!

WHO'S THE CHAP WAITING FOR HIM, ANYWAY?

THE 'CHAP' WAS ERIC PALMER, A PRIVATE DETECTIVE!

I SAW YOUR SIGNAL AS WE WERE COMING OFF, ERIC! YOU'VE GOT THE INFORMATION I WANTED?

RIGHT HERE, ROY...

...AND IT'S JUST WHAT I EXPECTED! THIS PROVES MY COUSIN, ARNIE MECKIFF, HASN'T CHANGED ONE BIT! HE'S STILL AN OUT-AND-OUT VILLAIN! THANKS A LOT, ERIC...

AS ROY RETURNED TO THE ROVERS DRESSING-ROOM...

ROY, INSPECTOR GOODALL WOULD LIKE A WORD WITH YOU ...ABOUT TREVOR BRINSDEN!

GOOD GRIEF! DON'T SAY HE'S STILL CAUSING TROUBLE!

I WOULDN'T BE SURPRISED, ROY! MY MEN DUMPED HIM WELL AWAY FROM THE STADIUM, AS YOU ASKED...

POLICE

'...BUT IT'S WHAT BRINSDEN SAID AS THEY DROVE AWAY THAT GOT ME WORRIED!'

TELL RACE I'LL GET HIM FOR THIS...

...THE ROVERS ARE MY LIFE! HE CAN'T STOP ME FROM WATCHING THEM!

POLICE

SO YOU THINK BRINSDEN IS A DANGEROUS FANATIC, EH, INSPECTOR? I GUESS YOU WANT TO GIVE ME A SPOT OF POLICE PROTECTION!

JUST FOR A FEW DAYS, ROY! A CONSTABLE WATCHING THE HOUSE ...THAT SORT OF THING...

IS IT THE END OF ROY OF THE ROVERS? SEE NEXT WEEK!

My marks out of ten for this story:

KEN HIBBITT and BILLY WRIGHT in colour!

ROY OF THE ROVERS

21st NOVEMBER, 1981 EVERY MONDAY

16p

ROY RACE HAD REFUSED POLICE PROTECTION, DESPITE BEING THREATENED BY FANATICAL FAN, *TREVOR BRINSDEN*, WHO HAD BEEN BANNED FROM *ROVERS'* HOME MATCHES. THE *MELCHESTER* PLAYER-MANAGER WAS MORE INTERESTED IN EXPOSING THE GET-RICH-QUICK SCHEMES OF HIS VILLAINOUS COUSIN, *ARNIE MECKIFF*. BUT, IN AN ALLEY NEAR MECKIFF'S DESERTED OFFICE . . .

LET'S SEE YOU 'DUMMY' YOUR WAY OUT OF **THIS ONE**, RACE!

I'LL NEVER GET BACK TO THE **MAIN** STREET IN TIME! I'VE ONLY ONE CHANCE!

CONTINUED ON COLOUR PAGES INSIDE . . .

©IPC Magazines Ltd., 1981

Australia 46c., New Zealand 45c., Malaysia $1 25, IR 23p (inc. VAT)

IS ROY BADLY HURT? YOU CAN FIND OUT NEXT WEEK!

My marks out of ten for this story:

ROY OF THE ROVERS

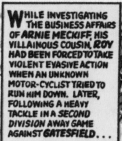

WHILE INVESTIGATING THE BUSINESS AFFAIRS OF ARNIE MECKIFF, HIS VILLAINOUS COUSIN, ROY HAD BEEN FORCED TO TAKE VIOLENT EVASIVE ACTION WHEN AN UNKNOWN MOTOR-CYCLIST TRIED TO RUN HIM DOWN. LATER, FOLLOWING A HEAVY TACKLE IN A SECOND DIVISION AWAY GAME AGAINST GATESFIELD...

SOMETHING'S WRONG WITH ROY'S SHOULDER! SOUNDS AS IF HE'S BADLY HURT!

OOOOOO-HHHHHH!

WHAT DID YE DO TO HIM, MAYNARD?

NOTHING! HONEST! IT WAS A FAIR TACKLE, MCKAY!

HE—HE'S RIGHT! IT WAS FAIR AND SQUARE! I—I MUST HAVE JARRED SOMETHING WHEN I FELL!

ARE YOU QUITE SURE, ROY?

I'M SURE IT WASN'T MAYNARD, ANYWAY! GUESS I BROKE SOMETHING WHEN I DIVED THROUGH THAT WINDOW, TO AVOID THE MOTOR-CYCLIST! BUT THAT'S MY BUSINESS... FOR NOW!

RACE IS TAKING HIMSELF OFF! WHAT A TERRIBLE BLOW FOR MELCHESTER!

YOU'VE GOT A CHANCE NOW, GATESFIELD! LET'S SEE YOU CASH IN ON IT!

ROVERS' SUBSTITUTE WAS MERVYN WALLACE, WHO HAD RECENTLY RECOVERED FROM A HAMSTRING INJURY...

MERVYN, I WANT YOU TO CHANGE PLACES WITH KENNY LOGAN...

...TELL HIM TO PUSH RIGHT UP INTO THE GATESFIELD BOX AND WAIT FOR THE OPENINGS!

OKAY, ROY! I'LL PASS IT ON...

AT FIRST, ROY'S GAMBLE SEEMED TO MEET WITH FAILURE...

OOOOOF!

LOGAN'S TOO SMALL AND LIGHT! NO DANGER AT ALL!

THEIR DEFENDERS ARE SMOTHERING HIS SKILLS!

AS THE BALL WAS PUMPED BACK INTO THE HOME GOALMOUTH...

NNNF!

HE'S GOT IN THE WAY OF JIMMY SLADE'S SHOT!

GET OUT OF IT, LOGAN!

NEXT WEEK: PROBLEMS MOUNT . . . INSIDE AND OUTSIDE OF THE CLUB!

ROY OF THE ROVERS

ROY WON A BATTLE, BUT NOT WITHOUT A SEVERE THREAT!

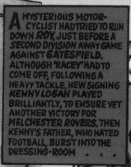

A MYSTERIOUS MOTOR-CYCLIST HAD TRIED TO RUN DOWN *ROY*, JUST BEFORE A *SECOND DIVISION* AWAY GAME AGAINST *GATESFIELD*. ALTHOUGH 'RACEY' HAD TO COME OFF, FOLLOWING A HEAVY TACKLE, NEW SIGNING KENNY LOGAN PLAYED BRILLIANTLY, TO ENSURE YET ANOTHER VICTORY FOR *MELCHESTER ROVERS*. THEN KENNY'S FATHER, WHO HATED FOOTBALL, BURST INTO THE DRESSING-ROOM . . .

I'M *ASKING* YOU FOR THE *LAST* TIME, KENNY . . .

. . . COME *BACK* WITH ME TO SCOTLAND, WHERE YOU *BELONG!* AND *YOU* STAY *OUT* OF THIS, RACE!

I'VE NO INTENTION OF INTERFERING, MISTER LOGAN! IT'S ALL UP TO KENNY . . .

. . . IN FACT, IF HE WANTS TO *LEAVE* MELCHESTER, I PROMISE THAT I'LL TRY AND *PERSUADE* THE DIRECTORS TO RELEASE HIM FROM HIS *CONTRACT!*

WELL, LAD . . . YOU *HEARD* HIM! WHAT DO YOU SAY?

FOR A LONG MOMENT, THE YOUNGSTER HESITATED. THEN . . .

I'M SORRY, DAD! I . . . I *COULDN'T* LEAVE THE ROVERS . . . *NOT* AFTER THE PERFORMANCE I TURNED IN TODAY! MELCHESTER'S MY *LIFE* NOW! I'D DIE OF BOREDOM, WORKING IN THE FAMILY BUSINESS!

MR. LOGAN GLARED AT ROY!

I MIGHT HAVE *KNOWN!* YOU . . . YOU'VE *POISONED* HIS MIND *AGAINST* ME, RACE—!

DAD, TAKE IT *EASY!* LET'S, ER . . . GO AND TALK ABOUT THIS *OUTSIDE* . . .

KENNY MANAGED TO ENTICE HIS FUMING FATHER INTO THE CAR PARK . . .

DO YOU THINK MISTER LOGAN WILL FINALLY *PERSUADE* THE LAD TO BECOME AN *ESTATE AGENT* INSTEAD OF A *FOOTBALLER*, ROY?

IF HE DOES, GOOD LUCK TO HIM! BUT THE ROVERS WILL *LOSE* ONE OF THEIR BEST PROSPECTS IN *YEARS!*

LATER, AS KENNY REJOINED THE REST OF THE TEAM IN THE PLAYERS' LOUNGE . . .

WELL, WHAT'S THE *VERDICT*, KENNY?

I'M *STAYING*, ROY . . .

. . . DAD'S FIGHTING A *LOSING* BATTLE AND HE *KNOWS* IT . . . BUT HE JUST *WON'T GIVE IN!* HE'S TALKING ABOUT CONSULTING HIS *SOLICITORS*, OR SOMETHING . . .

. . . AND I WOULDN'T *DREAM* OF DESCRIBING WHAT HE SAYS HE'S GOING TO DO TO *YOU*, IF EVER HE GETS HIS HANDS ON YOU!

IS VIC GUTHRIE FINISHED WITH MELCHESTER ROVERS? FIND OUT NEXT WEEK!

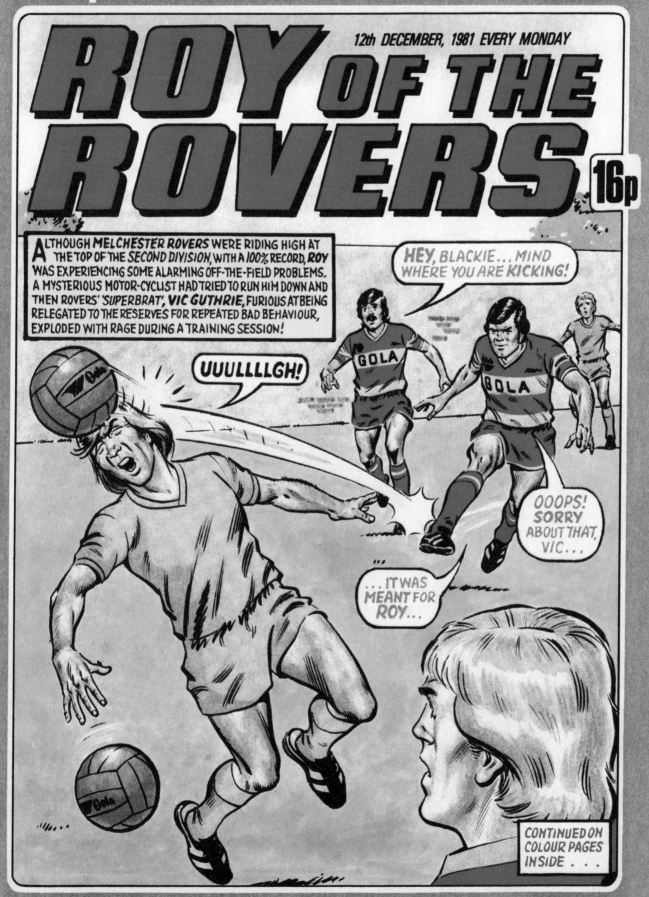

©IPC Magazines Ltd., 1981

Australia 46c.. New Zealand 45c.. Malaysia $1.25. IR 23p (inc. VAT)

ROY OF THE ROVERS

VIC GUTHRIE WAS FIRST ON THE SCENE!

ALTHOUGH MELCHESTER ROVERS WERE RIDING HIGH AT THE TOP OF THE SECOND DIVISION, ROY WAS EXPERIENCING SOME ALARMING, OFF-THE-FIELD PROBLEMS AND HAD MADE SOME BITTER ENEMIES. HE HAD RETURNED TO MELCHESTER STADIUM, LATE AT NIGHT, UNAWARE THAT HIS LIFE WAS IN DANGER. A FEW MINUTES AFTER THE ECHOES OF THE SHOT HAD CRASHED AND VIBRATED INTO SILENCE . . .

ROY, ARE YOU THERE? THAT...NOISE! IT SOUNDED LIKE A SHOT...

ROY!

THE ROVERS 'SUPERBRAT', VIC GUTHRIE, TOOK ONE LOOK AT THE SPRAWLING FIGURE... AND LUNGED FOR THE TELEPHONE!

...EMERGENCY! FIRE, POLICE, OR AMBULANCE?

POLICE...AND AN AMBULANCE! AND HURRY, FOR PETE'S SAKE...

...ROY RACE HAS BEEN SHOT!

FOLLOWING GUTHRIE'S CALL, THINGS HAPPENED VERY QUICKLY!

AN AMBULANCE! WITH A POLICE ESCORT!

IT MUST BE SOMEBODY IMPORTANT!

AMBULANCE

...ROY RACE? I...I CAN'T BELIEVE IT!

INTENSIVE CARE

CASUALTY

GANGWAY! MIND YOUR BACKS!

STUNNED CLUB OFFICIALS BEGAN TO ARRIVE AT MELCHESTER GENERAL HOSPITAL, WHERE THE ROVERS GENERAL MANAGER, BEN GALLOWAY, WAS BEING INTERVIEWED BY THE POLICE...

YOU...YOU'RE TREATING THIS AS ATTEMPTED MURDER, INSPECTOR?

FOR THE TIME BEING, MISTER GALLOWAY! CAN YOU THINK OF ANYONE WHO MIGHT HAVE A MOTIVE FOR WANTING TO TAKE A SHOT AT ROY?

...A FAN, OFFICIALS, PLAYERS...

...SUCH AS YOU, MISTER GUTHRIE? I UNDERSTAND THERE HAVE BEEN SOME PRETTY UGLY SCENES BETWEEN YOU AND ROY JUST RECENTLY!

THAT'S RIGHT, INSPECTOR! THAT'S WHY I WENT BACK TO THE STADIUM, TONIGHT...

...I WAS HOPING TO HAVE A FINAL, MAKE-OR-BREAK TALK WITH ROY, TO TRY AND CLEAR THE AIR AND... GOOD GRIEF! SURELY YOU HAVEN'T PUT ME ON YOUR LIST OF SUSPECTS?

ROY OF THE ROVERS

AT HALF-TIME, THE LATEST NEWS ON ROY'S CONDITION WAS BROADCAST!

ALL OVER THE WORLD, THE *CHRISTMAS PREPARATIONS* OF MILLIONS OF PEOPLE HAD BEEN SOURED BY THE NEWS THAT *ROY RACE* HAD BEEN SHOT BY AN UNKNOWN GUNMAN. NOW, AS ROY LAY IN HOSPITAL IN A COMA, HIS TEAM-MATES WERE TRYING TO TREAT A *LEAGUE MATCH* AGAINST *HOLVERTON* AS JUST ANOTHER GAME . . .

OOOOHHHH! RIGHT IN FRONT OF GOAL AND WITH ONLY THE 'KEEPER TO BEAT!

. . . AND *KENNY LOGAN* SLICED IT WIDE!

ROVERS SHOULD BE *THREE GOALS* UP BY NOW!

IT HAD BEEN A PAINFUL STRUGGLE FOR THE ROVERS AND THE SCORE WAS STILL 0-0 AT HALF-TIME, AS . . .

LADIES AND GENTLEMEN... BOYS AND GIRLS — WE HAVE JUST RECEIVED THE LATEST NEWS ABOUT ROY'S CONDITION!

SSSH!

LISTEN!

. . . ROY'S GENERAL CONDITION IS SATISFACTORY, BUT HE SHOWS NO SIGN OF RECOVERING CONSCIOUSNESS AND HAS FAILED TO RESPOND TO ANY KIND OF STIMULUS!

GOOD GRIEF!

I DON'T LIKE THE SOUND OF THAT!

IN THE ROVERS DRESSING-ROOM...

SORRY, BLACKIE, BUT I—I'M JUST NOT *WITH IT* TODAY! YOU MIGHT AS WELL PULL ME OFF!

WHY'S THAT, KENNY . . .

. . . IT'S SOMETHING TO DO WITH YOUR *FATHER,* ISN'T IT?

THE YOUNG SCOT NODDED MISERABLY...

EVERYONE KNOWS HOW MUCH MY DAD *HATES* ROY ... BECAUSE I PREFERRED TO PLAY FOR THE ROVERS, RATHER THAN WORK IN THE FAMILY BUSINESS! I JUST KEEP WONDERING IF *HE* HAD ANYTHING TO DO WITH THE *SHOOTING!*

WELL, *DON'T!* FEELING GUILTY WON'T BRING ROY OUT OF THAT *COMA!* IF YOU WANT TO MAKE THIS WHOLE, GHASTLY BUSINESS SEEM A LITTLE MORE BEARABLE, THERE'S ONLY *ONE* WAY YOU CAN DO IT...

A FEW MOMENTS INTO THE SECOND-HALF...

NICE INTERCEPTION BY LOGAN, BUT HE'S UNDER PRESSURE!

HE HASN'T A HOPE OF MAKING ANYTHING OF THIS! NOT AFTER HIS FIRST-HALF PERFORMANCE!

"... THE DOCTORS ARE TRYING EVERYTHING TO BRING HIM ROUND ..."

Will it be a HAPPY NEW YEAR for ROVERS?

ROY OF THE ROVERS

2nd JANUARY, 1982 EVERY MONDAY

16p

THERE WAS STILL NO CLUE TO THE IDENTITY OF THE *GUNMAN* WHO HAD STUNNED THE SOCCER WORLD BY SHOOTING AND INJURING *ROY RACE*. NOW, AS ROY LAY UNCONSCIOUS IN HOSPITAL, LIFE CONTINUED FOR *MELCHESTER ROVERS*, WITH AN AWAY GAME AGAINST *WAKEFORD* . . .

COME **ON**, ROVERS . . . YOU'RE **STRUGGLING!** SORT IT OUT!

CONTINUED ON COLOUR PAGES INSIDE . . .

©IPC Magazines Ltd., 1981

Australia 46c., New Zealand 45c., Malaysia $1.25, IR 23p (inc. VAT)

ROY OF THE ROVERS

9th JANUARY, 1982 EVERY MONDAY

16p

SIR ALF TO THE RESCUE!

ROY WAS *STILL LYING UNCONSCIOUS* IN HOSPITAL, AFTER BEING SHOT DOWN BY AN UNKNOWN GUNMAN, AND ALTHOUGH THEY WERE UNBEATEN IN THE *SECOND DIVISION,* THE PRESSURE WAS BEGINNING TO TELL ON *MELCHESTER ROVERS,* SO THE CLUB'S DIRECTORS HAD SENT FOR HELP... IN A *VERY BIG WAY!*

©IPC Magazines Ltd., 1982

Australia 46c., New Zealand 45c., Malaysia $1.25, IR 23p (inc. VAT)

MEANWHILE, IN THE RECEPTION LOUNGE...

...I DON'T HAVE TO REMIND YOU THAT WE'RE LUCKY TO GET HIM, GENTLEMEN! HAVING WON ALMOST EVERY HONOUR IN THE GAME—INCLUDING THE WORLD CUP—SIR ALF DOESN'T HAVE TO PROVE HIMSELF TO ANYONE, ANY MORE...

CHAMPIONS OF THE WORLD 1966

...SO I WANT YOU TO STRESS HOW GRATEFUL WE ARE THAT HE HAS AGREED TO HELP US THROUGH THE BIGGEST CRISIS THAT THIS CLUB HAS EVER FACED!

THEN!

YOU'D BETTER ROLL UP THE RED CARPET AGAIN, SAM! SIR ALF HAS GONE STRAIGHT OUT TO THE PITCH!

GOOD GRIEF...

...HE OBVIOUSLY LIKES TO GET STRAIGHT DOWN TO BUSINESS!

HEY, BLACKIE! THERE HE IS...

BLACKIE GRAY HAD BEEN APPOINTED TEMPORARY PLAYER-MANAGER IN ROY'S ABSENCE...

...WELCOME BACK, SIR ALF! I, ER...GUESS THE FIRST THING YOU'D LIKE TO DO IS HAVE A CHAT WITH THE PLAYERS!

YES, PLEASE, BLACKIE... AS SOON AS I'VE PAID MY RESPECTS TO THE DIRECTORS! YOU CAN FORGET THE 'SIR', BY THE WAY! 'ALF' WILL DO NICELY...

...AND WHILE I'M GONE, PERHAPS YOU'D BE KIND ENOUGH TO ORGANISE SOME PRACTICE! PASSING, HEADING, AND ANYTHING WHICH INVOLVES AGILITY! I WANT TO SEE HOW EVERYONE SHAPES UP!

HALF AN HOUR LATER, AS THE FORMER MANAGER OF ENGLAND RE-APPEARED...

WELL, I'LL BE—! HE'S WEARING A TRACK-SUIT ...AS IF HE INTENDS TO JOIN IN THE WORK-OUTS!

DON'T WORRY! I'LL BET HE'S KEPT HIMSELF FIT...

NOT SURPRISINGLY, THE ROVERS FOUND IT DIFFICULT TO CONCENTRATE!

HE'S WANDERING AROUND, WATCHING US!

AS IF HE'S ASSESSING OUR STRENGTHS AND WEAKNESSES!

I HAVEN'T GOT ANY WEAKNESSES

NEXT WEEK: A BITTER ARGUMENT BETWEEN ROVERS PLAYERS!

My marks out of ten for this story:

ROY OF THE ROVERS

VIC GUTHRIE'S GOOD WORK LOOKED LIKE GOING AGAINST HIM!

ROY RACE WAS STILL LYING UNCONSCIOUS IN HOSPITAL, AFTER BEING SHOT DOWN BY AN UNKNOWN GUNMAN, AND FORMER ENGLAND MANAGER, SIR ALF RAMSEY, HAD AGREED TO BECOME CARETAKER MANAGER OF MELCHESTER ROVERS. SIR ALF CAUSED AN IMMEDIATE SENSATION BY BRINGING BACK 'SUPERBRAT' VIC GUTHRIE—WHO HAD BEEN QUESTIONED BY THE POLICE ABOUT THE SHOOTING—FOR AN AWAY GAME AGAINST WESTBURY!

THEY'RE AWAY! COME ON NOW, WESTBURY!

LET'S SEE YOU SHATTER ROVERS' UNBEATEN RECORD!

IT'S HARD TO BELIEVE THIS IS MELCHESTER'S TWENTIETH LEAGUE GAME WITHOUT DEFEAT!

AND SIR ALF WILL WANT TO IMPROVE ON THAT! HE WON'T WANT THE ROVERS GETTING BEATEN AS SOON AS HE TAKES OVER!

YOU'RE ABSOLUTELY RIGHT, I WON'T!

SUDDENLY! ...A BREAK BY NOEL BAXTER! THAT'S RIGHT OUT OF RAMSEY'S BOOK OF RULES, ANYWAY!

EVERY PLAYER IN THE TEAM SHOULD BE PREPARED TO ATTACK... INCLUDING FULL-BACKS!

BUT A WESTBURY HEAD INTERCEPTED NOEL'S CROSS!

THE ROVERS WILL HAVE TO PRACTISE ON THAT ONE!

THEIR FORWARDS JUST WEREN'T LOOKING FOR THE BALL!

AND NOW WE'VE GOT MELCHESTER UNDER PRESSURE!

GREAT BALL! STRAIGHT INTO THE GAP LEFT BY BAXTER...

YOU MEAN THERE WAS A GAP! VIC GUTHRIE COVERED IT PERFECTLY!

OOOOOF!

NOW YOU KNOW WHY SIR ALF BROUGHT HIM BACK INTO THE TEAM!

BUT MELCHESTER WERE STILL SORTING THEMSELVES OUT AS WESTBURY TOOK A QUICK THROW...

NEAR POST, TERRY!

BAXTER, COME ON! I CAN'T COVER YOU ALL THE TIME!

ROY OF THE ROVERS

IT WAS A PUZZLED ROVERS AS THEY TOOK THE FIELD FOR THE SECOND-HALF!

ROY WAS STILL LYING UNCONSCIOUS IN HOSPITAL, AFTER BEING SHOT DOWN BY AN UNKNOWN GUNMAN, AND FORMER ENGLAND MANAGER, SIR ALF RAMSEY, HAD AGREED TO BECOME CARETAKER MANAGER OF MELCHESTER ROVERS. AT HALF-TIME, AGAINST WESTBURY, ROVERS WERE BEHIND 1-0 AND IN DANGER OF LOSING THEIR UNBEATEN LEAGUE RECORD. AS THE PLAYERS FACED THEIR NEW BOSS...

AN INTERESTING FIRST-HALF, LADS! I'VE MADE A FEW NOTES AND I EXPECT THERE ARE ONE OR TWO THINGS THAT YOU WOULD LIKE TO BRING UP, TOO!

YOU BET THERE ARE, ALF! FOR A START—!

BUT THIS IS NEITHER THE TIME, NOR THE PLACE! I MEAN, WE ARE STILL LEARNING ABOUT EACH OTHER, AREN'T WE? SO JUST GO OUT AND CONTINUE PLAYING YOUR NORMAL GAME, AND LET'S SEE WHAT HAPPENS!

MOMENTS LATER...

THE ROVERS LOOK A BIT THOUGHTFUL! I WONDER WHAT SIR ALF SAID TO THEM ABOUT THEIR FIRST-HALF PERFORMANCE?

THE SHORT ANSWER TO THAT IS... PRECISELY NOTHING!

BUT, AS IF THE ROVERS WERE RELIEVED TO ESCAPE WITHOUT A ROASTING FROM THE FORMER ENGLAND MANAGER...

THIS IS MORE LIKE THE OLD ROVERS... SMOOTH, PATIENT BUILD-UP! ALL THE PLAYERS HELPING EACH OTHER...

THEN!

OHHHHH! KENNY LOGAN ALMOST SNEAKED IN AT THE FAR POST!

CORNER TO MELCHESTER!

LOOK! SIR ALF'S WAVING TO VIC GUTHRIE! HE'S TELLING HIM TO GO UP FOR THE CORNER!

HE'S GONE UP, ALL RIGHT! THE SUPERBRAT'S STANDING ALMOST UNDER THE CROSSBAR!

THAT'S JUST WHAT JACKIE CHARLTON USED TO DO WHEN ALF WAS RUNNING THE ENGLAND TEAM!

WORRIED BY THE PRESENCE OF THE TALL, GANGLING CENTRE-BACK, THE WESTBURY 'KEEPER TRIED TO PUNCH THE CORNER-KICK AWAY, INSTEAD OF CATCHING IT!

HE'S ONLY HELPED THE BALL ON TO THE CROSSBAR!

OOOOOOF!

CLEAR THAT BALL, WESTBURY!

TOO LATE, PAL!

MERVYN WALLACE! IT'S THERRRRRE!

WESTBURY 1, MELCHESTER ROVERS 1!

THIS SHOULD BE INTERESTING! VIC GUTHRIE MADE THE GOAL, NOW LET'S SEE IF ANY OF THE ROVERS ATTEMPT TO CONGRATULATE HIM!

A LOT OF PEOPLE REGARD HIM AS ONE OF THE SUSPECTS!

GUTHRIE HAD BEEN INVOLVED IN A BITTER DISPUTE WITH ROY, JUST BEFORE THE SHOOTING...

NICE ONE, VIC! AS FAR AS I'M CONCERNED, YOU'RE JUST ANOTHER MEMBER OF THE TEAM... UNTIL EVENTS PROVE OTHERWISE!

VERY GENEROUS OF YOU, BLACKIE...

...BUT WE'LL WAIT UNTIL ROY RECOVERS! THEN YOU CAN ALL APOLOGISE TO ME TOGETHER!

OKAY... 'SUPERBRAT'! IF THAT'S THE WAY YOU WANT IT!

LATER, AFTER THE GAME HAD FIZZLED OUT INTO A 1-1 DRAW...

WE'RE STILL UNBEATEN IN THE LEAGUE, BUT FOR HOW MUCH LONGER?

I RECKON THE SHOCK OF WHAT HAPPENED TO ROY IS JUST GETTING THROUGH TO THE PLAYERS!

I WONDER HOW HE'S GETTING ON?

AT THAT MOMENT, IN THE INTENSIVE-CARE UNIT AT MELCHESTER GENERAL HOSPITAL...

WELL, WE'VE TRIED JUST ABOUT EVERYTHING! THE RECORDED VOICES OF THE RACE TWINS...

...EVEN A COMMENTARY ON THE WESTBURY GAME! BUT THERE'S STILL NO RESPONSE!

OH, R-ROY!

THEN, AS PENNY TURNED AWAY!

WAIT A MINUTE! I THOUGHT I—! I—I'M SURE I HEARD HIM GROAN!

SOMETHING'S HAPPENED, ALL RIGHT...

...THE LITTLE TEDDY WHICH MELINDA LEFT BEHIND! IT WAS JUST LYING ON THE BED A SECOND OR TWO AGO!

BUT NOW ROY IS GRASPING IT!

FANS WON'T WANT TO MISS SEEING WHAT HAPPENS NEXT WEEK!

My marks out of ten for this story:

ROY OF THE ROVERS

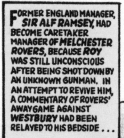

FORMER ENGLAND MANAGER, *SIR ALF RAMSEY*, HAD BECOME CARETAKER MANAGER OF *MELCHESTER ROVERS*, BECAUSE *ROY* WAS STILL UNCONSCIOUS AFTER BEING SHOT DOWN BY AN UNKNOWN GUNMAN. IN AN ATTEMPT TO REVIVE HIM, A COMMENTARY OF ROVERS' AWAY GAME AGAINST *WESTBURY* HAD BEEN RELAYED TO HIS BEDSIDE . . .

THE LITTLE *TOY* THAT MELINDA LEFT LYING ON THE BED . . . DID ANYONE *PUT* IT IN ROY'S HAND?

N-NO, DOCTOR!

THEN HE MUST HAVE PICKED IT UP *HIMSELF!* QUICK, PENNY!

WHAT . . . WHAT SHALL I DO?

SPEAK TO HIM! SHOUT IN HIS EAR . . .

. . . ANYTHING! PERHAPS THE VOICE HE KNOWS BEST WILL BRING HIM TO *FULL CONSCIOUSNESS!*

ROY, IT'S ME! IT'S PENNY! OH, PLEASE OPEN YOUR EYES! SPEAK TO ME, ROY . . . PLEASE!

BUT . . .

IT—IT'S NO USE! IF THERE *WAS* ANY . . . CONSCIOUS SPARK, IT'S *GONE* AGAIN!

OH, N-NO!

ALL RIGHT, PENNY! NEVER MIND . . .

. . . AT LEAST WE GOT *SOME* RESPONSE! —A GLIMMER OF HOPE! WE'LL TRY THE SAME EXPERIMENT WITH MELCHESTER'S *NEXT* MATCH! IT'S A HOME GAME, ISN'T IT?

YES! AGAINST . . . KEYSBROUGH, I THINK . . .

AS THE 'GLIMMER OF HOPE' WAS RELAYED TO THE MELCHESTER FANS WHO KEPT CONSTANT VIGIL OUTSIDE THE HOSPITAL . . .

. . . APART FROM *THAT*, THERE'S LITTLE CHANGE IN *ROY'S* CONDITION! SO WHY DON'T YOU ALL GO HOME, LADIES AND GENTLEMEN?

NO THANKS, DOC! WE'RE STAYING RIGHT HERE UNTIL ROY COMES ROUND . . .

. . . NO MATTER HOW LONG IT TAKES!

MEANWHILE, THE SEARCH FOR A LEAD TO THE IDENTITY OF THE UNKNOWN GUNMAN WAS CONTINUING . . .

THE POLICE HAVE HAD ANOTHER CHAT WITH VIC *GUTHRIE* . . . BUT I DOUBT IF IT GOT THEM ANYWHERE!

I'LL BET THE ONLY PERSON WHO CAN *REALLY* HELP THEM IS *ROY!* AND HE'S NOT IN A POSITION TO MAKE A STATEMENT!

THE ROVERS 'SUPERBRAT' LEFT HIS HOME, SHORTLY AFTERWARDS...

BOOOOO!

CUT THAT OUT! IF THE POLICE HAD A CASE AGAINST VIC, THEY WOULD HAVE ARRESTED HIM BY NOW!

AND HE'S STILL DOING A GOOD JOB FOR THE ROVERS!

LATER, AT MELCHESTER STADIUM, VIC JOINED THE OTHER ROVERS FOR A TACTICAL TALK WITH SIR ALF...

WELL, LADS, I'VE NOW HAD AN OPPORTUNITY TO ASSESS THE STRENGTHS AND WEAKNESSES OF THE VARIOUS PLAYERS! IT'S TIME I PUT MY, ER, IDEAS INTO PRACTICE...

...KENNY LOGAN, I WANT YOU TO PLAY A MORE POSITIVE PART, FORAGING UP FRONT! TRY AND WIN BALLS FOR VERNON ELIOT AND PACO DIAZ, WHO'LL BE PLAYING SLIGHTLY BEHIND, AND ON EITHER SIDE OF YOU...

...BLACKIE WILL LINK UP WITH THEM IN THE MIDDLE OF THE PARK...WHILE JIMMY SLADE AND MERVYN WALLACE MUST DROP BACK TO TRY AND CUT OUT ANY THROUGH BALLS...

...TOWARDS THE REGION OF THE PENALTY AREA! WE SHOULD WIND UP WITH A FORMATION...

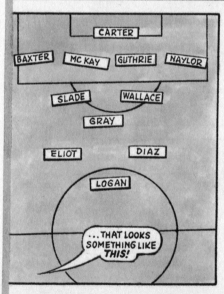

CARTER

BAXTER McKAY GUTHRIE NAYLOR

SLADE WALLACE

GRAY

ELIOT DIAZ

LOGAN

...THAT LOOKS SOMETHING LIKE THIS!

BUT IT'S NOT A RIGID FORMATION! YOU SHOULD BE READY TO INTERCHANGE ROLES AT ANY TIME DURING THE GAME! AND, REMEMBER...

...IT ONLY TAKES ONE BAD PASS TO MAKE THE WHOLE THING BREAK DOWN!

AS THE TALK ENDED AND THE PLAYERS SPLIT UP FOR SOME CIRCUIT TRAINING...

...HE EVEN EXPECTS NOEL BAXTER AND STEVE NAYLOR TO BE RAIDING WINGERS!

WHY NOT, TAFF? ALF'S ONLY ASKING US TO ATTACK AND PASS THE BALL ACCURATELY...WHICH IS WHAT WE USED TO DO FOR ROY!

ON THE DAY OF THE KEYSBROUGH GAME, AN ATMOSPHERE OF TENSION HUNG OVER MELCHESTER STADIUM...

...THE RADIO IS TURNED UP HIGH AT ROY'S BEDSIDE. SO MUMS AND DADS, BOYS AND GIRLS, GET THOSE VOCAL CHORDS WELL OILED! SHOUT YOUR HEADS OFF FOR THE ROVERS! LET'S SEE IF YOU CAN WAKE HIM UP!

...AND LET'S HOPE THAT SIR ALF'S TACTICS WORK! AS LONG AS ROVERS SCORE THE GOALS, WE'LL SHOUT OURSELVES SILLY!

AYE! THEY'LL HEAR US ON THE MOON!

WILL ROY BE REVIVED? BE SURE TO FIND OUT NEXT WEEK!

My marks out of ten for this story:

ROY OF THE ROVERS

SIR ALF'S TACTICS LOOKED AS THOUGH THEY WERE GOING TO PAY OFF!

FORMER ENGLAND MANAGER, SIR ALF RAMSEY, HAD BECOME CARETAKER MANAGER OF MELCHESTER ROVERS, BECAUSE ROY WAS STILL UNCONSCIOUS AFTER BEING SHOT BY AN UNKNOWN GUNMAN. NOW A TREMENDOUS EFFORT WAS BEING MADE TO REVIVE HIM AS, AGAINST 'KEYSBORG' ROVERS PARADED SIR ALF'S TACTICS BEFORE THEIR OWN SUPPORTERS, FOR THE FIRST TIME.

LOOK AT THE WAY THE ROVERS ARE LINING UP!

I'VE NEVER SEEN A FORMATION LIKE THAT BEFORE!

NOR ME! IT'S A SORT OF... FOUR-TWO-ONE-ONE-TWO FORMATION!

WE'VE HEARD OF TRYING TO CONFUSE THE OPPOSITION, SIR ALF, BUT THIS IS RIDICULOUS!

LET'S JUST WAIT AND SEE, EH? YOU NEVER KNOW... IT JUST MIGHT PRODUCE A GOAL OR TWO!

BLACKIE GRAY WAS HOPING THAT THE GAME WOULD PRODUCE AN AVALANCHE OF GOALS!

THE CROWD'S A BIT SUBDUED! WE'VE GOT TO GET OUR FANS ROARING FOR US ...LOUDER THAN THEY'VE EVER DONE BEFORE...

MELCHESTER! MELCHESTER!

...FOR ROY'S SAKE!

AND AT MELCHESTER GENERAL HOSPITAL, WHERE A COMMENTARY ON THE GAME WAS BEING RELAYED TO ROY'S BEDSIDE...

HERE WE GO, EVERYBODY! KEEP YOUR FINGERS CROSSED!

...AND ROVERS HAVE LOST NO TIME PUTTING SIR ALF'S TACTICS TO THE TEST! NOEL BAXTER IS JUST STORMING UP THAT RIGHT-WING...

...IT'S NOT A GOOD PASS, BUT KENNY LOGAN IS CHASING IT LIKE A LITTLE TERRIER!

THIS IS THE KIND OF FORAGING ROLE THAT SIR ALF HAS ASKED HIM TO PLAY...

...AND IT'S HAVING AN EFFECT ALREADY! KENNY'S WON THE BALL ...AND FED IT TO PACO DIAZ...

...NOW OUT TO STEVE NAYLOR— ROVERS' DEFENDER! STEVE SHOULD HIT IT ON THE RUN, LOW AND TO THE FAR POST...

IS THIS WHAT WE'VE ALL BEEN WAITING FOR? SEE NEXT WEEK!

My marks out of ten for this story:

ROY OF THE ROVERS

IT WAS THE SIGHT THAT ALL THE FOOTBALL WORLD HAD BEEN WAITING FOR!

FORMER ENGLAND MANAGER, SIR ALF RAMSEY, HAD BECOME CARETAKER MANAGER OF MELCHESTER ROVERS AFTER ROY WAS SHOT DOWN BY AN UNKNOWN GUNMAN. IN AN ATTEMPT TO REVIVE HIM, A COMMENTARY OF ROVERS' HOME MATCH AGAINST KEYSBOROUGH WAS RELAYED TO HIS BEDSIDE... WITH SENSATIONAL RESULTS!

ROY RACE! ROY RACE!

UUUHHHNNNNN!

IT—IT WORKED! THE CHEERS OF THE MELCHESTER FANS HAVE PENETRATED TO ROY'S SUBCONSCIOUS!

HE'S COMING OUT OF THE COMA!

WHAT... WHERE AM I? PENNY!

ROY... ROY!

NO, PENNY!

HE MUSTN'T HAVE TOO MUCH EXCITEMENT... NOT YET, ANYWAY! IT'S VITAL HIS RECOVERY IS *GRADUAL!*

BUT, I—I'VE WAITED FOR THIS MOMENT FOR WEEKS!

I KNOW... BUT YOU'LL HAVE TO WAIT A LITTLE LONGER... UNTIL WE'VE MADE SOME TESTS!

IN THE MEANTIME, PENNY, I'M SURE YOU'LL WANT TO CONVEY THE GOOD NEWS TO TWO *OTHER* PEOPLE WHO HAVE BEEN WAITING!

ROY... MELINDA!

MUMMY, YOU'RE CRYING! WHAT'S THE MATTER?

HAS DADDY WOKEN UP YET?

YES, MY DARLINGS... HE'S AWAKE! *YOUR DADDY HAS COME BACK TO US!*

OH, PENNY!

MEANWHILE, AT MELCHESTER STADIUM, WHERE THE ROVERS WERE STILL LEADING TWO-NIL...

OOOOHHHH! JIMMY SLADE ALMOST MADE IT *THREE!*

SIR ALF'S TACTICS ARE WORKING LIKE A DREAM!

BE SURE NOT TO MISS NEXT WEEK'S 'GOALDEN' EPISODE!

ROY OF THE ROVERS

THERE WAS AN ATMOSPHERE OF UTTER PANDEMONIUM!

FORMER ENGLAND MANAGER, SIR ALF RAMSEY, HAD BECOME 'CARETAKER' MANAGER OF MELCHESTER ROVERS, AFTER ROY WAS SHOT DOWN BY AN UNKNOWN GUNMAN. A COMMENTARY OF ROVERS' HOME MATCH AGAINST KEYSBOROUGH RELAYED TO ROY'S BED-SIDE, HELPED TO BRING HIM OUT OF A COMA... AND THE NEWS HAD AN ELECTRIFYING EFFECT ON THE MELCHESTER PLAYERS!

GOOOALL!

PACO'S DONE IT FROM THE FREE-KICK!

FIVE-NIL TO THE ROVERS!

AS KEYSBOROUGH'S TACKLING BECAME MORE AND MORE DESPERATE!

AAAAAGH!

THEY ALMOST DRAGGED KENNY LOGAN'S SHIRT OFF!

PENALTY TO MELCHESTER!

DUNCAN McKAY SLAMMED IN THE SPOT-KICK!

NUMBER SIX! YESSSSSS!

WE WANT SEVEN! WE WANT SEVEN!

IN AN ATMOSPHERE OF UTTER PANDEMONIUM, MERVYN WALLACE OBLIGED THE MELCHESTER FANS!

HURAAAAY!

SEVEN-NIL! I FEEL ALMOST SORRY FOR KEYSBOROUGH!

I WONDER IF ROY IS LISTENING TO THIS?

SURE ENOUGH, AT MELCHESTER GENERAL HOSPITAL...

'...BLACKIE GRAY... AND IT'S THERE! SEVEN-NIL! I... I MEAN, EIGHT! GOOD GRIEF, I'M BEGINNING TO LOSE COUNT!'

IT SOUNDS AS IF THE ROVERS MIGHT BE GETTING ON TOP, ROY!

AYE...

...WHAT'S... WHAT'S THE RECORD FOR THE... MOST GOALS SCORED BY... ONE TEAM IN A... FOOTBALL LEAGUE GAME, PENNY?

ROY RACE! YOU'VE BEEN UNCONSCIOUS FOR SEVEN WEEKS AND ALL YOU CAN THINK ABOUT IS FOOTBALL!

BUT SOMEONE SOON CAME UP WITH THE ANSWER...

A CHAP IN THE NEXT WARD IS A FOOTBALL FANATIC, ROY! HE SAYS IT'S THIRTEEN GOALS... BY NEWCASTLE, STOCKPORT AND TRANMERE!

SO... ROVERS NEED ANOTHER... SIX TO... BREAK THE RECORD...

WOWEEEEEEEEEE!

FOURTEEN-NIL! THEY'VE **DONE** IT!

THE ROVERS HAVE SET A **NEW LEAGUE RECORD!**

AS THE REFEREE BLEW FOR FULL-TIME, SECONDS LATER...

HURRAAAAAAAAAAAY!

LET THEM **GO**, LADS! THIS IS **ONE** PITCH INVASION I WOULDN'T MIND JOINING IN MYSELF!

AYE! WE'LL FORGIVE THEM! JUST THIS **ONCE!**

SOMEHOW, THE MATCH COMMENTATOR STRUGGLED UP TO SIR ALF RAMSEY...

SIR ALF, WOULD YOU SAY THAT THE ROVERS ARE BEGINNING TO SETTLE INTO YOUR STYLE OF PLAY?

OH, YES! ALTHOUGH THEY MISSED A FEW CHANCES, I'M QUITE PLEASED WITH TODAY'S PERFORMANCE...

...BUT YOU MUST REMEMBER THAT THE FOUNDATIONS WERE ALREADY THERE! I HAVE MERELY BUILT ON THE METHODS OF A MAN WHO HAS CREATED ONE OF THE FINEST ATTACKING MACHINES IN FOOTBALL...

...AND I'LL BE DELIGHTED WHEN HE GETS BACK HERE AND PUTS ME **OUT OF A JOB!**

HEH! HEH! GOOD OLD ALF! ...EH, PENNY?

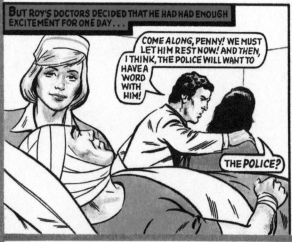

BUT ROY'S DOCTORS DECIDED THAT HE HAD HAD ENOUGH EXCITEMENT FOR ONE DAY...

COME ALONG, PENNY! WE MUST LET HIM REST NOW! AND THEN, I THINK, THE POLICE WILL WANT TO HAVE A WORD WITH HIM!

THE POLICE?

YES! THEY ARE HOPING THAT ROY CAN GIVE THEM A CLUE TO THE **IDENTITY...**

INTENSIVE CARE UNIT

...OF THE MAN WHO **TRIED TO KILL HIM!**

NEXT WEEK: A SUSPECT IS ARRESTED AT THE AIRPORT!

My marks out of ten for this story:

ROY OF THE ROVERS

THE REST OF THE ROVERS WENT TO VISIT ROY RACE . . . EXCEPT VIC GUTHRIE!

MELCHESTER ROVERS HAD STORMED TO AN INCREDIBLE 14-0 VICTORY OVER KEYSBOROUGH, SETTING A NEW LEAGUE RECORD, AND A LIVE COMMENTARY ON THE GAME HAD HELPED ROY TO RECOVER FROM A GUNSHOT WOUND. OUTSIDE MELCHESTER GENERAL HOSPITAL, WHERE A CROWD OF FANS HAD KEPT CONSTANT VIGIL . . .

CELEBRITIES HAVE BEEN ARRIVING ALL DAY TO CONGRATULATE ROY ON HIS RECOVERY...

...EVEN THE MINISTER FOR SPORT HAS MADE A PERSONAL VISIT!

BUT HERE COME THE PEOPLE WHO ROY WILL REALLY WANT TO SEE...

...IT'S THE ROVERS!

HURRAAAAAAAAY!

CONGRATULATIONS ON THE NEW RECORD, LADS!

THANKS! BUT DON'T FORGET TO GIVE SIR ALF RAMSEY A BIT OF CREDIT!

AND DON'T FORGET TO GIVE ROY OUR GOOD WISHES!

IT'LL BE A PLEASURE!

HEY, MISTER...DIDN'T YOU NOTICE SOMETHING? WHY DIDN'T YOU ASK THEM WHERE HE WAS?

HUH? ASK THEM WHERE WHO WAS?

VIC GUTHRIE OF COURSE! HE WASN'T THERE!

HEY, THAT'S RIGHT! AND GUTHRIE IS SUPPOSED TO BE ON THE POLICE LIST OF SUSPECTS!

INSIDE THE HOSPITAL, PENNY RACE WAS WAITING FOR THE ROVERS...

HOW'S THAT HUSBAND OF YOURS, PENNY? IS HE GOING TO BE FIT FOR SATURDAY?

NOT QUITE, BLACKIE...

...BUT THE DOCTORS ARE DELIGHTED WITH HIM! HE'S COMING ALONG FINE!

GREAT!

BUT HE'S, ER... TIED UP AT THE MOMENT!

THE POLICE! OF COURSE... THIS IS THE FIRST CHANCE THEY'VE HAD TO QUESTION HIM ABOUT THE SHOOTING!

DON'T MISS FURTHER DEVELOPMENTS IN NEXT WEEK'S EPISODE!

ROY OF THE ROVERS

"WELL, ROY . . . ACCORDING TO OUR LATEST TESTS, YOU ARE DISGUSTINGLY FIT!"

MELCHESTER ROVERS WERE STILL UNBEATEN IN THE SECOND DIVISION, DESPITE THE FACT THAT ROY WAS IN HOSPITAL, RECOVERING FROM A GUNSHOT WOUND. NOW THE TASK OF HUNTING DOWN HIS WOULD-BE KILLER HAD BEGUN AND, ONE MORNING, SENSATIONAL HEADLINES GREETED THE NATION!

MELCHESTER'S VIC GUTHRIE INTERCEPTED AT CITY AIRPORT!

SPORTSNEWS — RUNAWAY 'SUPERBRAT' HELPING POLICE WITH INQUIRIES INTO ROY RACE SHOOTING

SPORTS — WHY DID HE BUY A TICKET TO BASRAN?

A TELEVISION REPORTER INTERVIEWED CHIEF INSPECTOR MANNING, THE DETECTIVE IN CHARGE OF THE CASE...

CHIEF INSPECTOR, IS GUTHRIE UNDER ARREST? HAS HE BEEN CHARGED WITH THE ATTEMPTED MURDER OF HIS OWN MANAGER?

LET'S JUST SAY THAT HE FIGURES STRONGLY IN OUR INVESTIGATIONS! MY OFFICERS WOULD ALSO LIKE A CHAT WITH ONE OR TWO OTHER PEOPLE...

...SUCH AS **ARTHUR LOGAN**... ...**TREVOR BRINSDEN**... ...AND ROY'S COUSIN, **ARNIE MECKIFF!**

UNFORTUNATELY, ALL THESE GENTLEMEN SEEM TO BE LYING LOW AT THE MOMENT!

THE POLICE WOULD ALSO LIKE TO INTERVIEW **ELTON BLAKE** — THE ACTOR WHO WAS SACKED FROM MIDLAND TELEVISION'S TWICE-WEEKLY SERIES ABOUT THE ROVERS! BLAKE, IT SEEMS, IS VISITING RELATIVES IN CANADA...

...BUT NOW LET'S GO OVER TO MELCHESTER GENERAL HOSPITAL, WHERE THE NEWS ABOUT ROY RACE IS GETTING BETTER AND **BETTER!**

AT THAT MOMENT, INSIDE THE HOSPITAL...

WELL, ROY... ACCORDING TO OUR LATEST TESTS, YOU ARE DISGUSTINGLY FIT! SO YOU MIGHT AS WELL GO HOME!

HOME? I—I DON'T BELIEVE IT!

IT'S NOT SO SURPRISING! THE WOUND WASN'T SERIOUS AND ONCE YOU HAD RECOVERED CONSCIOUSNESS, THE WORST WAS OVER!

THAT'S **FABULOUS!**

I'VE BROUGHT YOUR CLOTHES, ROY...

ROY IS READY FOR HIS RETURN TO THE ROVERS!

My marks out of ten for this story:

ROY OF THE ROVERS

DOCTORS CLEARED ROY! HE'S BACK IN CHARGE!

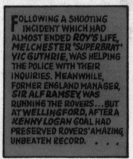

THE LONG-AWAITED NEWS WAS CARRIED BY EVERY BRANCH OF THE MEDIA...

...SO IT'S WELCOME BACK, ROY RACE! ON A MORE SERIOUS NOTE, VIC GUTHRIE IS STILL BEING QUESTIONED BY THE POLICE! GUTHRIE WAS INTERCEPTED AT MELCHESTER AIRPORT, AS HE WAS ABOUT TO BOARD A FLIGHT TO THE MIDDLE-EASTERN STATE OF BASRAN...

...THE POLICE ARE ALSO TALKING TO ARTHUR LOGAN, FATHER OF THE MELCHESTER STRIKER, KENNY LOGAN! MISTER LOGAN WAS TRACED TO A HOTEL IN THE NORTH OF SCOTLAND, EARLY THIS MORNING!

HOTEL SPORAN

POLICE

AT HOME, ROY WAS TRYING TO ANSWER THE MANY LETTERS AND CARDS FROM WELL-WISHERS...

DO YOU THINK LOGAN COULD HAVE ANYTHING TO DO WITH IT, ROY?

HE MADE SOME NASTY THREATS, PENNY! BUT SO DID MY COUSIN, ARNIE MECKIFF! THERE'S BEEN NO SIGN OF HIM SINCE I THREATENED TO EXPOSE THAT LAND-RACKET HE WAS OPERATING...

YET ANOTHER SUSPECT WAS TREVOR BRINSDEN, A TROUBLESOME FAN WHO HAD BEEN BANNED FROM ROVERS' HOME GAMES! THE FOLLOWING SATURDAY...

KEEP A SHARP EYE OUT FOR BRINSDEN, MEN! I WOULDN'T BE SURPRISED IF THAT FANATIC CHOSE THIS GAME TO MAKE HIS RETURN TO THE SCENE!

RACEY!

MAIN GATE →

MANY OF THE FANS HEADING FOR MEL PARK HAD NO HOPE OF GETTING IN...

THE GROUND'S NEARLY PACKED ALREADY!

WE MISSED YOU ROY!

I CAN'T WAIT TO SEE OLD ROY!

SAME HERE! I HAD A HORRIBLE FEELING THAT I'D NEVER SEE HIM WALK INTO THIS STADIUM AGAIN!

OLE! RACEY!

WELCOME BACK ROY!

IN THE ROVERS DRESSING-ROOM...

OKAY, LADS... NO TEAM-TALK TODAY! I'M JUST GOING TO SIT BACK AND WATCH YOU HANG ON TO THAT UNBEATEN RECORD!

IT WON'T BE FOR THE WANT OF TRYING ...BOSS!

AS THE ROOM EMPTIED...

BEN, I—I KNOW IT SOUNDS CRAZY, BUT I'VE GOT BUTTERFLIES IN THE STOMACH!

I'M NOT SURPRISED, ROY! IT'S A LONG TIME SINCE YOU FACED A MELCHESTER CROWD!

HERE COME THE TEAMS! THEY'RE GOING TO FORM A GUARD OF HONOUR FOR ROY!

WE WANT RACEY!

WE WANT RACEY!

ROVERS

RACEY

GOLA

WE WANT RACEY!

THEY'RE ALL YOURS, ROY!

...AND THE MAN WHO HAD CHEATED DEATH WENT OUT TO FACE NEW GLORY... AND AN UNCERTAIN FUTURE!

DON'T MISS THIS EMOTIONAL MOMENT ... IN NEXT WEEK'S EPISODE!

My marks out of ten for this story:

ROY OF THE ROVERS

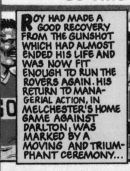

ROY HAD MADE A GOOD RECOVERY FROM THE GUNSHOT WHICH HAD ALMOST ENDED HIS LIFE AND WAS NOW FIT ENOUGH TO RUN THE ROVERS AGAIN. HIS RETURN TO MANAGERIAL ACTION, IN MELCHESTER'S HOME GAME AGAINST DARLTON, WAS MARKED BY A MOVING AND TRIUMPHANT CEREMONY...

HURRAAAAAAAAY!

GOOD GRIEF, I'VE NEVER HEARD SUCH *CHEERING!*

IT'S ALL FOR YOU, RACEY!

NICE TO HAVE YOU BACK, ROY!

FOR HE'S A JOLLY GOOD FELLLLOW...

I CAN HARDLY HEAR MYSELF *SPEAK!* THIS IS A MOMENT THAT ROY RACE WILL REMEMBER FOR THE REST OF HIS LIFE!

THE COMMENTATOR WAS RIGHT!

THERE'S ONLY ONE ROYYY RACE...

WE MISSED YOU RACEY

SO THIS IS THE LITTLE 'SURPRISE' BEN GALLOWAY MENTIONED... THOUSANDS OF FANS, ARMED WITH *LETTER-CARDS!*

AS THE SEA OF CARDS RIPPLED AND CHANGED...

YES, THIS STADIUM IS ALMOST LIKE A 'HOME' TO ME...COMPLETE WITH SIXTY THOUSAND GUESTS...

WELCOME HOME

...AND I LOVE THEM ALL!

WE SHOULD HAVE KNOWN OLD ROY WAS INDESTRUCTIBLE!

RIGHT, IT'S *YOUR* TURN NOW, LADS! LET'S SEE YOU FOLLOW THAT WITH A *RESOUNDING VICTORY!*

YOU'VE GOT IT, ROY!

LET'S GO!

THEY'RE AWAAAAAY!

I FEEL ALMOST SORRY FOR DARLTON!

WITH ROY BACK ON THE BENCH, THERE'LL BE NO STOPPING THE ROVERS!

ROY OF THE ROVERS

IGNORING CALLS FROM HIS TEAM-MATES, DUNCAN McKAY "STEAMED" FOR GOAL!

A MASSIVE CROWD HAD WELCOMED ROY BACK TO MANAGERIAL DUTY, FOLLOWING HIS RECOVERY FROM A GUNSHOT WOUND. BUT THE EXPECTED CELEBRATION VICTORY OVER DARLTON FAILED TO MATERIALISE, AS MELCHESTER ROVERS TURNED ON A CHAOTIC DISPLAY OF SKILLED, BUT RECKLESS FOOTBALL!

YOURS, CHARLIE!

WHAT A WAY TO CLEAR A CROSS... A BACK-HEADER TO THE 'KEEPER!

Y-YOU IDIOT, NOEL!

CHARLIE CARTER WAS STILL SOME WAY FROM THE BALL AS A DARLTON PLAYER NIPPED IN!

AAAAH!

IT'S THERE! THREE-ONE TO DARLTON!

THIS IS CRAZY!

BLACKIE GRAY TRIED TO RESTORE ORDER!

COME ON, LADS... CONCENTRATE! WE'RE SUPPOSED TO BE MAKING THIS A SPECIAL OCCASION FOR ROY... REMEMBER?

AYE BLACKIE'S RIGHT! LET'S SETTLE DOWN AND START PLAYING LIKE PROFESSIONALS!

DUNCAN McKAY SEEMED DETERMINED TO FOLLOW UP HIS WORDS... WITH ACTION!

GREAT TACKLE! THAT'S BETTER, DUNCAN!

UUULLGH!

THE SCOT'S SHOWING THEM THE WAY!

WITH YOU, DUNC!

JIMMY'S FREE ON YOUR LEFT!

LAY IT OFF, MAN!

YE MUST BE JOKING...

...APART FROM PENALTIES, AH HAV'NAE SCORED ONE THIS SEASON!

HE-HE'S HAD A GO... FROM THIRTY YARDS!

GLORY BE... IT'S IN! THREE-TWO!

HURRAAAAAAY!

NEXT WEEK: THE NET IS CLOSING IN ON ROY'S WOULD-BE KILLER!

ROY OF THE ROVERS

A FLUKE CLEARANCE PRODUCED A STUNNING GOAL!

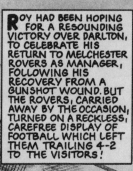

ROY HAD BEEN HOPING FOR A RESOUNDING VICTORY OVER DARLTON, TO CELEBRATE HIS RETURN TO MELCHESTER ROVERS AS MANAGER, FOLLOWING HIS RECOVERY FROM A GUNSHOT WOUND. BUT THE ROVERS, CARRIED AWAY BY THE OCCASION, TURNED ON A RECKLESS, CAREFREE DISPLAY OF FOOTBALL WHICH LEFT THEM TRAILING 4-2 TO THE VISITORS!

OOOO-OOOPS

OHHH! SCRAMBLED CLEAR BY CHARLIE CARTER!

AND THE BALL IS LOOSE! DARLTON COULD *STILL* MAKE IT *FIVE-TWO!*

NOT IF UNCLE NOEL CAN HELP IT! *WAH-HAAY!*

WELL, THAT'S *ONE* WAY OF CLEARING THE BALL!

THE BALL CARRIED TO VERNON ELIOT... WHO SIMPLY HELPED IT ON ITS WAY!

THAT'S HEADING FOR THE FAR POST!

NNNNE!

AND... KENNY LOGAN! *YESSSSSS!*

FOUR-*THREE!* THE BALL DIDN'T TOUCH THE GROUND FROM THE MOMENT IT HIT CHARLIE CARTER!

NOW I'VE SEEN *EVERYTHING!* THIS GAME GETS CRAZIER AND CRAZIER!

BUT THE LADS ARE STILL IN IT, ROY... EVEN IF THEY'VE NO RIGHT TO BE!

BLACKIE GRAY WAS DOING HIS BEST TO ORGANISE THE ROVERS...

NOW, MERV ...LET'S STRING TOGETHER SOME PASSES! KEEP THAT BALL *MOVING!*

WITH PLEASURE, BLACKIE!

MERVYN WALLACE'S HIT-OR-MISS THUNDERBOLT SEEMED TO HAVE 'EQUALISER' WRITTEN ALL OVER IT. BUT...

SAAAVED!

CORNER TO MELCHESTER! THIS COULD BE THEIR LAST CHANCE!

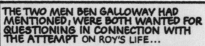

NEXT PART "...AND WHEN YOU RUN OUT ON SATURDAY, CREEP, I'LL BE THERE!"

My marks out of ten for this story:

ROY OF THE ROVERS

MELCHESTER ROVERS HAD 'CELEBRATED' ROY'S RECOVERY FROM A GUNSHOT WOUND BY LOSING THEIR UNBEATEN LEAGUE RECORD! BUT WITH ROVERS ALMOST CERTAIN TO GAIN PROMOTION FROM THE 2nd DIVISION, NOBODY REALLY CARED. NOW ROY WAS PREPARING FOR ANOTHER LONG-AWAITED EVENT...

ONLY ANOTHER FIVE MINUTES ON THE 'MULTI-GYM', ROY!

THEN WE'LL CHECK A FEW THINGS BEFORE WE GO ON TO THE NEXT STAGE...

LATER, AS ROY TOOK PART IN A PRACTICE MATCH...

THERE'S THE 'ROCKET'! A BIT OFF TARGET, BUT IN PERFECT WORKING ORDER...

BUT THIS COULD BE CRUCIAL! IF ROY'S MEMORY OF THE MURDER ATTEMPT MAKES HIM RELUCTANT TO ATTEMPT A HEADER...

...HE'LL HAVE TO SURRENDER THE BALL TO THE OPPOSING SIDE!

BUT...

LET'S GO, YOU REDS!

HE DIDN'T SPARE HIMSELF! LIKE THE ROY OF OLD, THAT WAS COMPLETELY AND UTTERLY INSTINCTIVE!

THE TWO MEN WHO WERE PAYING SUCH CLOSE ATTENTION TO ROY, WERE DOCTORS...

WHAT'S NEXT, GENTLEMEN?

JUST ONE OR TWO FINAL TESTS... SUCH AS YOUR BLOOD-PRESSURE, ROY!

AND I'D LIKE TO HAVE A LOOK AT THE BULLET-WOUND SCAR TISSUE...

COME ON, FOR PETE'S SAKE! PUT ME OUT OF MY MISERY!

WELL, I WON'T SAY THAT THIS IS ONE OF THE MOST REMARKABLE RECOVERIES IN MEDICAL HISTORY...

...BUT THERE IS ABSOLUTELY NO REASON WHY YOU SHOULDN'T PLAY AGAINST HUNTERFORD, ON SATURDAY!

WAHOOOOOO!

NOT SURPRISINGLY, THE NEWS WAS DEVOURED BY THE MEDIA...

...ROY'S RETURN TO ACTIVE DUTY COULDN'T HAVE BEEN MORE TIMELY! OBVIOUSLY WORRIED ABOUT HIS *FATHER*, KENNY LOGAN IS PLAYING WELL BELOW HIS NORMAL FORM...

...KENNY'S FATHER IS, OF COURSE, JUST ONE OF THE PEOPLE BEING QUESTIONED BY THE POLICE ABOUT THE RECENT ATTEMPT ON ROY'S LIFE...

I RECKON IT'S ABOUT TIME THEY STOPPED TALKING AND *CHARGED* SOMEONE!

ELTON BLAKE, THE FORMER STAR OF THE TELEVISION SERIES ABOUT THE ROVERS, ARRIVED AT MELCHESTER POLICE STATION TODAY—!

IT CAN'T BE *BLAKE*, PENNY! I MEAN, HE'D HARDLY GIVE HIMSELF UP IF *HE* WAS THE CULPRIT!

THE ACTOR'S VOICE SHOOK WITH FURY...

IF YOU THINK I'M THE KIND OF PERSON WHO GOES AROUND SHOOTING FOOTBALL MANAGERS AND TRYING TO RUN PEOPLE DOWN ON MOTOR-BIKES, YOU MUST BE *CRAZY*!

WHO DO *YOU* THINK TRIED TO KILL YOU, ROY?

I'M PUTTING MY MONEY ON *TREVOR BRINSDEN*—THAT HOOLIGAN I BANNED FROM THE GROUND! THERE HASN'T BEEN A SIGN OF HIM SINCE THE SHOOTING...

HAVE YOU SEEN THIS MAN?

...SO IT LOOKS AS IF HE'S SKIPPED TOWN! AND AN *INNOCENT* MAN WOULDN'T *NEED* TO HIDE, WOULD HE?

BUT BRINSDEN WASN'T FAR AWAY!

THAT'S IT! THAT'S WHERE I'LL GET IN!

BY NOW, EVEN HIS CLOSEST FRIENDS WOULD HAVE HAD DIFFICULTY IN RECOGNISING HIM...

NOT A BAD SKETCH OF IT ALL! LOOKS GOOD WITH ALL THE STUFF ABOUT MELCHESTER I'VE COLLECTED OVER THE YEARS!

WHATEVER'S HAPPENED, I'M *STILL* ROVERS' *GREATEST FAN*...

...AND WHEN YOU RUN OUT ON SATURDAY, CREEP, *I'LL* BE THERE! YOU'LL *NEVER* GET RID OF OLD TREVOR! NEVER, NEVER, *NEVER*!

DON'T MISS WHAT HAPPENS IN NEXT WEEK'S EPISODE!

My marks out of ten for this story:

ROY OF THE ROVERS

IN THE CROWD WAS A 'FAMILIAR' FACE!

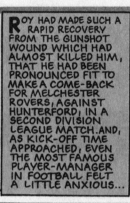

ROY HAD MADE SUCH A RAPID RECOVERY FROM THE GUNSHOT WOUND WHICH HAD ALMOST KILLED HIM, THAT HE HAD BEEN PRONOUNCED FIT TO MAKE A COME-BACK FOR MELCHESTER ROVERS, AGAINST HUNTERFORD, IN A SECOND DIVISION LEAGUE MATCH. AND, AS KICK-OFF TIME APPROACHED, EVEN THE MOST FAMOUS PLAYER-MANAGER IN FOOTBALL FELT A LITTLE ANXIOUS...

WELL, LADS... HOW DO I LOOK?

GREAT!

LIKE YOU'VE NEVER BEEN AWAY, RACEY!

THE QUESTION IS, HOW DO YOU *FEEL*?

I...I'M NOT SURE. THERE'S SOMETHING AT THE BACK OF MY MIND THAT I—!

HEY, *ROY!* WE'RE READY WHEN YOU ARE!

ROY GRINNED GRATEFULLY AT FRANK DOUGLAS, THE HUNTERFORD SKIPPER...

THANKS ALL THE SAME, FRANK, BUT THERE'LL BE NO GUARD OF HONOUR STUFF TODAY. IT'S BACK TO SERIOUS SOCCER BUSINESS FOR ALL OF US!

HURRAAAAAAY!

IT'S TIME I STARTED *EARNING* THOSE CHEERS, TOO; WITH MY *BOOTS!*

EVEN SO, THE EXCITEMENT OF ROY'S RETURN WAS TOO MUCH FOR SOME OF HIS FANS!

GOOD LUCK, ROY! SCORE THE FIRST ONE FOR ME!

FOR YOU, ROY! EVERYONE IN MY CLASS HAS SIGNED IT!

WHAT ON EARTH...

ROCK ON ROY

ROY'S HOPES OF A 'QUIET' COME-BACK WERE TOTALLY SHATTERED!

ROY RACE! ROY RACE!

WHAT A MAN!

I'D LIKE TO GET MY HANDS ON THE RAT WHO TRIED TO KILL HIM!

WELL, THE POLICE HAVE ROUNDED UP THE VARIOUS SUSPECTS... WITH THE EXCEPTION OF *TREVOR BRINSDEN!*

THE HOOLIGAN THAT ROY BANNED FROM MEL PARK! I WONDER WHERE *HE* IS?

HEE! HEEEEE!

ROY OF THE ROVERS

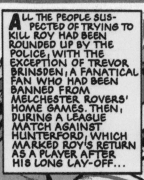

ALL THE PEOPLE SUSPECTED OF TRYING TO KILL ROY HAD BEEN ROUNDED UP BY THE POLICE, WITH THE EXCEPTION OF TREVOR BRINSDEN, A FANATICAL FAN WHO HAD BEEN BANNED FROM MELCHESTER ROVERS' HOME GAMES. THEN, DURING A LEAGUE MATCH AGAINST HUNTERFORD, WHICH MARKED ROY'S RETURN AS A PLAYER AFTER HIS LONG LAY-OFF...

YOU...YOU'RE *CRAZY!* I'M NOT TREVOR BRINSDEN! I DON'T EVEN *LOOK* LIKE HIM!

YOU DO UNDER THAT BEARD, PAL...

AND THAT LONG HAIR!

THE LITTLE CREEP JUST COULDN'T KEEP AWAY!

GRAB HIM!

NAAOWWGH!

COME HERE!

LOOK OUT!

THE TERRIFIED YOUTH'S BID FOR FREEDOM DIDN'T GET FAR!

NO YOU DON'T, MY LAD! YOU'VE GOT A DATE WITH THE POLICE...

YEEAAAAAAH!

...*AFTER* WE'VE FINISHED WITH YOU!

G-GET THEM OFF! HELP MEEEEE!

FILTHY LITTLE KILLER...

WE...WE'LL NEVER REACH HIM IN TIME! THOSE FANS ARE SO ANGRY, THEY'LL TEAR BRINSDEN APART!

BUT AT THAT MOMENT...

ROY, IT'S *TREVOR BRINSDEN!* SOUNDS LIKE THEY'VE CAUGHT HIM!

WHAAAT?

OVER BY THE HUNTERFORD GOAL!

ROY DIDN'T HESITATE!

LOOK AT OLD ROY! HE CAN'T WAIT TO GET AT THAT SPOTTY LITTLE MURDERER!

OUT OF MY WAY! LET ME THROUGH!

GO *ON,* RACEY!

LEAVE HIM *ALONE,* YOU CRAZY IDIOTS!

WHAT THE—?

BUT, ROY, IT'S *BRINSDEN*—THE RAT WHO TRIED TO *KILL* YOU!

NEXT SATURDAY: A VITAL CLUE TO THE IDENTITY OF THE WOULD-BE MURDERER!

ROY OF THE ROVERS

"THEY'RE *CRAZY!* I DON'T EVEN KNOW HOW TO *FIRE* A GUN!"

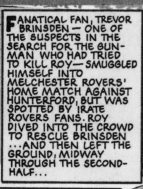

FANATICAL FAN, TREVOR BRINSDEN — ONE OF THE SUSPECTS IN THE SEARCH FOR THE GUNMAN WHO HAD TRIED TO KILL ROY — SMUGGLED HIMSELF INTO MELCHESTER ROVERS' HOME MATCH AGAINST HUNTERFORD, BUT WAS SPOTTED BY IRATE ROVERS FANS. ROY DIVED INTO THE CROWD TO RESCUE BRINSDEN ...AND THEN LEFT THE GROUND, MIDWAY THROUGH THE SECOND-HALF...

TREVOR CASSIDY, THE SUBSTITUTE, HAS TAKEN OVER WHERE ROY LEFT OFF!

THAT'S A BEAUTIFUL BALL TO PACO DIAZ!

NICE ONE, PACO!

AND IT'S *THERE!* THREE-*NIL!*

A LESS THAN ENTHUSIASTIC ROAR HAD GREETED THE SPANISH SUPERSTAR'S GOAL...

MADRE MIA! MAYBE THEY GET SO USED TO SEE ME SCORING, THEY NOT GET EXCITED ANYMORE!

IT'S GOT NOTHING TO DO WITH YOU, PACO! AT ANY OTHER TIME, THE FANS WOULD HAVE RAISED THE ROOF...

...BUT THIS TREVOR BRINSDEN BUSINESS HAS GOT THEM GUESSING. ROY THINKS HE'S FIGURED OUT WHO TRIED TO KILL HIM NOW... AND ALL THE SUSPECTS ARE DOWN AT THE POLICE STATION!

AT THAT MOMENT...

ROY, WHAT YOU'RE ASKING IS HIGHLY IRREGULAR! IT- IT'S LIKE SOMETHING OUT OF A SHERLOCK HOLMES MOVIE!

I KNOW INSPECTOR. BUT NONE OF THE SUSPECTS HAVE BROKEN DOWN UNDER QUESTIONING, SO FAR... SO WHAT HAVE YOU GOT TO *LOSE?*

AND SO, MOMENTS LATER...

HERE THEY COME... ALL THE PEOPLE WHO HAVE THREATENED TO 'GET EVEN' WITH ME, FOR ONE REASON OR ANOTHER...

A HUSH FELL OVER THE INTERVIEW ROOM, AS ROY'S GAZE ROVED THE FIVE SUSPECTS...

COULD IT BE *YOU,* TREVOR? OUR *FANS* CERTAINLY SEEMED TO THINK SO!

THEY... THEY'RE *CRAZY!* I DON'T EVEN KNOW HOW TO *FIRE* A GUN!

NEXT WEEK: IT'S A KNOCKOUT!

ROY OF THE ROVERS

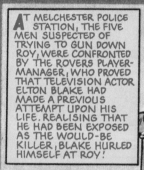

AT MELCHESTER POLICE STATION, THE FIVE MEN SUSPECTED OF TRYING TO GUN DOWN ROY, WERE CONFRONTED BY THE ROVERS PLAYER-MANAGER, WHO PROVED THAT TELEVISION ACTOR ELTON BLAKE HAD MADE A PREVIOUS ATTEMPT UPON HIS LIFE. REALISING THAT HE HAD BEEN EXPOSED AS THE WOULD-BE KILLER, BLAKE HURLED HIMSELF AT ROY!

YOU'RE *LYING*, RACE! YOU'RE TRYING TO *DESTROY* ME, LIKE YOU DID BEFORE—!

ROY, LOOK OUT!

IT'S ALL RIGHT, INSPECTOR...

...I'M NOT STANDING WITH MY *BACK* TO HIM THIS TIME!

UUUUGGH!

SORRY ABOUT THAT... BUT I THINK I'VE EARNED THE RIGHT TO TAKE AT LEAST *ONE* PUNCH AT HIM...

YOU SAVED US THE TROUBLE, ROY. ALL RIGHT, CONSTABLE....*TAKE HIM AWAY!*

AS BLAKE WAS HAULED FROM THE INTERVIEW ROOM...

HE WAS ALWAYS TOP OF OUR LIST, ROY... ALTHOUGH WE'VE STILL GOT TO ESTABLISH, BEYOND ANY DOUBT, THAT HE WAS RESPONSIBLE FOR THE SHOOTING. BUT I THINK WE CAN BREAK HIM DOWN NOW...

BUT... *WHY?* WHY DID HE TRY TO *KILL* ME?

I UNDERSTAND THAT THE TELEVISION SERIES ABOUT THE ROVERS WAS BLAKE'S LAST CHANCE OF BECOMING A REALLY BIG STAR! IF HE CONVINCED HIMSELF THAT *YOU* HAD HIM REMOVED FROM THE SERIES... NEED I SAY MORE, ROY?

I TOLD YOU IT WASN'T ME, INSPECTOR! SO HOW ABOUT LETTING US OUT OF HERE?

SORRY, MISTER MECKIFF! THERE'S A LITTLE MATTER OF TRYING TO SELL AUSTRALIAN SWAMPLAND AS 'VALUABLE BUILDING PLOTS'!

IT WAS ROY WHO HAD EXPOSED HIS VILLAINOUS COUSIN'S BOGUS LAND AGENCY...

I SHOULD HAVE PLUGGED YOU MYSELF, RACE!

AND YOU'RE NICE TO KNOW, TOO, ARNIE...

IN NEXT WEEK'S EPISODE: A GOAL OF PURE GENIUS!

ROY OF THE ROVERS

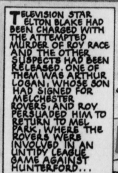

TELEVISION STAR ELTON BLAKE HAD BEEN CHARGED WITH THE ATTEMPTED MURDER OF ROY RACE AND THE OTHER SUSPECTS HAD BEEN RELEASED. ONE OF THEM WAS ARTHUR LOGAN, WHOSE SON HAD SIGNED FOR MELCHESTER ROVERS, AND ROY PERSUADED HIM TO RETURN TO MEL PARK, WHERE THE ROVERS WERE INVOLVED IN AN UNTIDY LEAGUE GAME AGAINST HUNTERFORD...

IT'S ROY... WITH KENNY LOGAN'S FATHER!

A MAN WHO HATES FOOTBALL... AND HATES ROY EVEN MORE FOR SIGNING ON HIS SON!

ARTHUR LOGAN HAD HOPED THAT HIS SON WOULD DEDICATE HIMSELF TO THE FAMILY ESTATE AGENCY BUSINESS...

RACE, I DON'T KNOW WHY I LET YOU TALK ME INTO COMING HERE!

YOU'RE FREE TO GO WHENEVER YOU LIKE, MISTER LOGAN... BUT JUST REMEMBER THAT YOUR SON IS DOWN THERE...

...ALL I ASK IS THAT YOU TAKE A GOOD LOOK AT THE WAY HE IS 'WASTING' HIS LIFE...

KENNY!

AAAUUUNF!

PATHETIC! THAT KID JUST CAN'T SEEM TO PUT HIS GAME TOGETHER TODAY...

MOMENTS LATER, KENNY MISSED ANOTHER CHANCE TO PUT PRESSURE ON HUNTERFORD...

COME ON, LOGAN... THAT CROSS MISSED EVERYBODY!

HE'S GOT WORSE SINCE HIS FATHER ARRIVED...

THAT'S IT! OLD MAN LOGAN'S PRESENCE HAS UNSETTLED HIM!

NOT FOR MUCH LONGER, ARTHUR LOOKS AS IF HE'S HAD ENOUGH...

ALREADY TRAILING 2-0, HUNTERFORD WERE MAKING LITTLE ATTEMPT TO ENTERTAIN THE FANS...

WHAT A ROTTEN CLEARANCE! IT HARDLY REACHED THE HALF-WAY LINE...

GET UNDER IT, MELCHESTER!

NEXT WEEK: MELCHESTER'S LAST MATCH IN THE SECOND DIVISION!

ROY OF THE ROVERS

"WELL, MISTER LOGAN, IS KENNY STAYING WITH ROVERS, OR GOING HOME WITH YOU?"

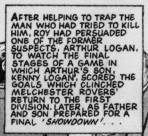

AFTER HELPING TO TRAP THE MAN WHO HAD TRIED TO KILL HIM, ROY HAD PERSUADED ONE OF THE FORMER SUSPECTS, ARTHUR LOGAN, TO WATCH THE FINAL STAGES OF A GAME IN WHICH ARTHUR'S SON KENNY LOGAN, SCORED THE GOALS WHICH CLINCHED MELCHESTER ROVERS' RETURN TO THE FIRST DIVISION. LATER, AS FATHER AND SON PREPARED FOR A FINAL 'SHOWDOWN'...

KENNY...ROY HAS GIVEN HIS PERMISSION FOR ME TO INTERVIEW YOU FOR TELEVISION! I'VE SET UP THE CAMERA OUT ON THE PITCH...

AYE, WELL... YE'LL HAVE TO WAIT A MINUTE! I'M HAVING A WEE CHAT WITH MY *DAD*, FIRST!

TELEVISION, EH? THEY'RE TRYING TO TURN YOU INTO A 'STAR' ALREADY!

THAT'S NOT THE *ONLY* REASON I JOINED THE ROVERS, DAD... TO BECOME FAMOUS! THIS IS A GREAT CLUB AND I'M *PROUD* TO BE WEARING MELCHESTER'S COLOURS...

HALF-AN-HOUR LATER, AS ROY HIMSELF WAS NEARING THE END OF A TELEVISION INTERVIEW...

CAN YOU GIVE US ANY IDEA AS TO WHAT HAPPENED AT THE POLICE STATION, ROY?

SORRY, BRIAN, I'M LEAVING IT TO THE POLICE TO ISSUE A STATEMENT! RIGHT NOW, I WANT TO TRY AND FORGET ABOUT THE WHOLE, MESSY BUSINESS...

...APART FROM ARTHUR LOGAN, THAT IS! SO IF YOU'LL EXCUSE ME, BRIAN, I THINK HE'D LIKE A WORD...

WELL, MISTER LOGAN, IS KENNY STAYING WITH THE ROVERS, OR GOING HOME WITH YOU? LIKE I SAID... HE'S FREE TO DO AS HE LIKES!

AYE, I BELIEVE THAT NOW! AND I MUST ADMIT I'VE NEVER SEEN THE LAD APPROACH ANYTHING WITH SUCH PRIDE AND—AND DEDICATION...

...AND IT'S OBVIOUS THAT YOU DIDN'T ENTICE HIM AWAY FROM ME. BUT THAT DOESN'T MEAN THAT I *APPROVE* OF WHAT HE'S DONE! MY FEELINGS ABOUT MELCHESTER ROVERS ...AND *FOOTBALL* IN GENERAL... HAVEN'T CHANGED...

...SO LOOK AFTER HIM, RACE! AND IF EVER THE LAD WANTS TO COME BACK TO SCOTLAND... AND ENTER THE FAMILY BUSINESS... I'LL WELCOME HIM WITH OPEN ARMS!

FAIR ENOUGH, MISTER LOGAN...

NEXT WEEK: VIC GUTHRIE STARTS OFF LIKE TOO MUCH OF A "NICE GUY"!

ROY OF THE ROVERS

"WHAT'S THE MATTER WITH GUTHRIE? WHAT A PATHETIC TACKLE!"

ALREADY ASSURED OF PROMOTION TO THE FIRST DIVISION, MELCHESTER ROVERS HAD NO INTENTION OF 'COASTING' THEIR LAST MATCH OF THE SEASON, AGAINST ROTHERTON. ROVERS WERE LEADING, 3-0, WHEN ROY BROUGHT ON A FAMILIAR FIGURE IN PLACE OF NAT GOSDEN...

VIC GUTHRIE... THE MELCHESTER 'SUPERBRAT'!

ONE OF THE MEN ORIGINALLY SUSPECTED OF TRYING TO KILL ROY!

GUTHRIE WAS ASKING FOR IT! HE MADE SOME PRETTY NASTY THREATS AGAINST ROY, WHEN HE WAS DISCIPLINED...

HE CAN THINK HIMSELF LUCKY ROY'S GIVING HIM A CHANCE TO MAKE A FRESH START...

GUTHRIE WAS SOON IN ACTION...

NOW MAKE THE MOST OF IT, GUTHRIE!

SHOW US THAT YOU'RE STILL OUR BEST CENTRAL DEFENDER!

BUT...

AAAUUNN!

WHAT A PATHETIC TACKLE! IT WOULDN'T HAVE STOPPED A FOURTH DIVISION STRIKER!

AND IT'S THERE! ROTHERTON HAVE PULLED ONE BACK!

DON'T BLAME CHARLIE CARTER! GUTHRIE'S MISTAKE LEFT HIM UTTERLY EXPOSED...

MOMENTS LATER, AS GUTHRIE TRIED TO CLEAR A CROSS!

ANOTHER HALF-HEARTED EFFORT!

THE BALL'S LOOSE! MAKE IT TWO, ROTHERTON!

OHHHHH! WHAT A SAVE!

CHARLIE CARTER GOT THE SUPERBRAT OUT OF TROUBLE, THAT TIME!

WHAT'S THE MATTER WITH GUTHRIE?

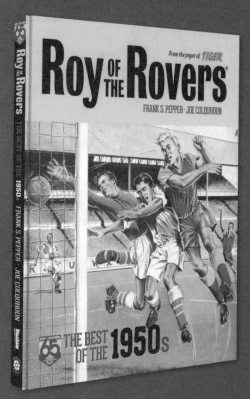

THE BEST OF THE 1950s
FRANK S. PEPPER · JOE COLQUHOUN

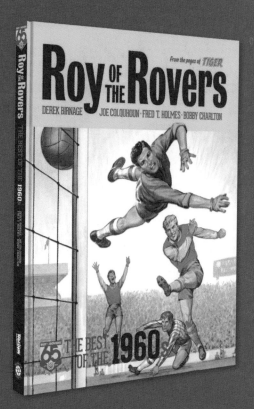

THE BEST OF THE 1960s
DEREK BIRNAGE · JOE COLQUHOUN
FRED T. HOLMES · BOBBY CHARLTON

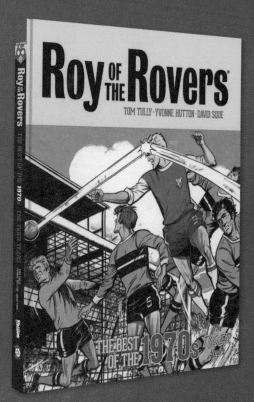

THE BEST OF THE 1970s
THE TIGER YEARS
TOM TULLY · YVONNE HUTTON · DAVID SQUE

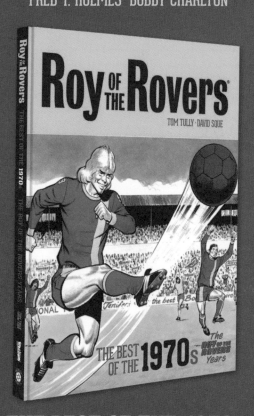

THE BEST OF THE 1970s
THE ROY OF THE ROVERS YEARS
TOM TULLY · DAVID SQUE

... I CAN SAY, WITHOUT BOASTING, THAT WE DON'T MISS A THING AT MELCHESTER! IF ANY LAD WITH GENUINE *SOCCER* ABILITY COMES TO THIS CLUB, WE'LL *RECOGNISE* IT, AND DO OUR BEST TO DEVELOP HIS TALENT TO THE *FULL* POTENTIAL!

THAT'S A LOAD OF *RUBBISH* AND RACE *KNOWS IT!* YOU ASK HIM ABOUT *TERRY DRAKE!*

WHAT THE—?

YOU MADE THE *BIGGEST* MISTAKE OF YOUR LIFE WITH OUR *TERRY,* RACE! AND HE'S GOING TO *PROVE* IT... ON *SATURDAY...* WHEN *BURNDEAN* COME TO MEL PARK!

IF HE *DOES,* MISTER DRAKE, *I'LL* BE THE *FIRST* TO CONGRATULATE HIM!

AS THE MAN WAS HUSTLED AWAY BY CLUB OFFICIALS...

DRAKE! NOW, LET ME SEE... WOULD THAT BE *NORMAN* DRAKE, THE FATHER OF THE LAD WHO WAS AN *APPRENTICE* WITH US, ABOUT TWO YEARS AGO?

YOU'VE GOT A GOOD MEMORY, BLACKIE...

...TERRY DRAKE CAME TO US WITH THE *HIGHEST* RECOMMENDATIONS. FOR HIS AGE, HE WAS ONE OF THE MOST PROMISING ATTACKING MIDFIELDERS I'D EVER SEEN...

'TROUBLE WAS, HE *KNEW* IT. AND, WHEN HIS *SKILL* COULDN'T GET HIM OUT OF TROUBLE, HE USED *OTHER* MEANS!'

YOU *DELIBERATELY* CHOPPED HIM FROM *BEHIND,* TERRY!

AWW, COME ON... IT WAS AN *ACCIDENT!*

'TERRY WASN'T VERY POPULAR **OFF** THE FIELD, EITHER. HE USED EVERY DODGE IN THE BOOK TO AVOID HIS FAIR SHARE OF THE APPRENTICES' WORK-LOAD...'

'SO, WHEN THE TIME CAME TO EITHER OFFER TERRY A CONTRACT, OR LET HIM GO... I HAD NO CHOICE!'

...YOU'RE OFFERING **HIM** A CONTRACT, AREN'T YOU? WHAT'S SO DIFFERENT ABOUT ME?

IN TERMS OF **SKILL,** TERRY, NOTHING! YOU BOTH PLAY THE SAME TYPE OF GAME, ON THE LEFT SIDE OF MIDFIELD...

...BUT THE OTHER LAD HAS SOMETHING THAT YOU DON'T APPEAR TO HAVE **HEARD** OF, TERRY! PLAIN, ORDINARY **DEDICATION!**

BUT—!

I'M SORRY, SON!

'MR. DRAKE WASN'T JUST SORRY... HE WAS **FURIOUS!** HE WAS WAITING FOR TERRY OUTSIDE THE STADIUM...'

DON'T WORRY ABOUT IT, TERRY! MELCHESTER ROVERS AREN'T THE ONLY FOOTBALL CLUB IN THE WORLD...

...WE'LL TAKE YOUR TALENTS SOMEWHERE **ELSE!**

AND THEY TOOK THEM TO **BURNDEAN,** EH, ROY?

RIGHT **VIA** A NON-LEAGUE CLUB! A FEW WEEKS AGO, TERRY DRAKE FORCED HIS WAY INTO 'DEAN'S FIRST-TEAM! THE SPORTS WRITERS ARE RAVING ABOUT HIM...

IF HE'S AS BRILLIANT AS THEY SAY HE IS, MAYBE I **DID** MAKE A MISTAKE!

WELL, HIS OLD MAN SAYS YOU DID, ROY! AND HE'S GOING TO KEEP **ON** SAYING IT ...TO ANYONE WHO WILL **LISTEN!**

IN THE DAYS THAT FOLLOWED, MR. DRAKE EVEN MANAGED TO GET HIMSELF ON TELEVISION...

WE WOULD LIKE TO KNOW WHAT YOUR **SON** THINKS ABOUT ALL THIS, MISTER DRAKE! BUT HE **REFUSES** TO MAKE ANY COMMENT!

ROY RACE ISN'T SAYING MUCH, EITHER...

...BECAUSE HE *KNOWS* HE WAS IN THE *WRONG!* MY LAD'S GOING TO MAKE HIM LOOK *SILLY* IN FRONT OF *SIXTY THOUSAND* PEOPLE ...AND *I'LL* BE THERE TO *SEE* IT!

IT WASN'T JUST NORMAN DRAKE WHO TURNED UP AT MELCHESTER STADIUM, THE FOLLOWING SATURDAY!

GATE B

BURNDEAN! BURNDEAN!

BURN

THE TERRY DRAKE FAN CLUB! HIS OLD MAN HAS ROUNDED UP EVERY MEMBER OF THE FAMILY HE CAN FIND!

WHEN BURNDEAN RAN OUT...

ROVE

HURAAAAAY! THAT'S MY BOY! SHOW THEM WHAT THEY *MISSED,* TERRY LAD!

MAKE IT A *DAY* OF *DISASTER* FOR ROY RACE!

BURNDEAN

THE ROVERS WERE ALREADY WARMING UP...

I THOUGHT YOUNG DRAKE WAS ON HIS WAY OVER HERE THEN, ROY ...TO HAVE A *WORD* WITH YOU!

BURNDEAN

HIS DAD HAS SAID ENOUGH FOR *BOTH* OF THEM! HE'S TURNED AN *ORDINARY* LEAGUE MATCH INTO A KIND OF PERSONAL *VENDETTA!*

AS THE GAME GOT UNDER WAY...

LET'S JUST HOPE IT *DOESN'T* GET OUT OF HAND!

THAT'S *GREAT* RUNNING BY TERRY DRAKE! HE'S MADE A BREAK ALREADY!

GO ON, OUR KID!

RTES STE SOU CRAIG MIDDLETO

BUT!

AAAOWWGH!

MERVYN WALLACE HAS NAILED HIM ...AND THE REF *DIDN'T* LIKE IT!

HE'S AWARDED A FREE-KICK TO BURNDEAN!

QUICK ONE, 'DEAN!

COME ON! LET'S WATCH THIS MARKING! WE DON'T NEED TWO PEOPLE SHADOWING DRAKE!

ROY'S YELL WAS IGNORED BY THE MELCHESTER DEFENDERS...

THEY'VE IGNORED THE 'DEAN NUMBER TEN, TOO!

HE'S LOOKING FOR TERRY DRAKE...

...AND FOUND HIM! OHHHH! WHAT A SHOT!

IT'S THERE!

NORMAN DRAKE AND HIS RELATIVES WENT WILD WITH DELIGHT!

YESSS! I TOLD YOU, DIDN'T I? THIS PROVES THAT RACE SHOULD HAVE SIGNED OUR TERRY!

YIPPEEEEE!

LET'S HAVE ANOTHER, OUR KID!

BUT THE RESTART WAS INTERRUPTED, AS...

MERVYN WALLACE IS GOING OFF! HE MUST HAVE INJURED HIMSELF WHEN HE MADE THAT TACKLE ON TERRY DRAKE!

ROY'S BRINGING ON YOUNG ALAN LYNCH!

ALAN DESERVES HIS CHANCE! HE'S BEEN GETTING A LOT OF GOALS FOR THE RESERVES...

TAKING MERVYN WALLACE'S PLACE ON THE LEFT, THE YOUNG SUBSTITUTE MADE AN UNEASY START...

HE WAS WAY OUT OF POSITION THEN!

AND TERRY DRAKE SPOTTED IT! HE'S THROUGH AGAIN!

CHARLIE'S CLEARANCE LED TO YET ANOTHER MELCHESTER ATTACK AND...

ALAN LYNCH! HE'S GOT THE LAST TOUCH TO THAT LOOSE BALL...

...AND WRAPS IT UP FOR THE ROVERS!

HURAAA-AAAAY!

AT FULL-TIME...

NEVER MIND, OUR TERRY! YOU WERE STILL THE BEST PLAYER ON THE PARK!

YOU'VE GOT TO HAND IT TO OLD MAN DRAKE—LOYAL TO THE LAST! AND I DON'T BLAME HIM!

NORMAN DRAKE WAS STILL SHOUTING AS ROY ENTERED THE MELCHESTER VISITORS' LOUNGE, AN HOUR LATER...

COME ON THEN, RACE... ADMIT IT! LETTING OUR TERRY GO WAS THE BIGGEST BLUNDER YOU EVER MADE—!

DAD, FOR PETE'S SAKE, LEAVE IT! YOU DON'T KNOW WHAT YOU'RE TALKING ABOUT!

TERRY DRAKE'S OUTBURST SHOCKED HIS FATHER INTO SILENCE!

I WASN'T THE ONLY APPRENTICE AT MELCHESTER, TWO YEARS AGO! IT'S ABOUT TIME YOU MET THE PLAYER THAT ROY CHOSE TO RETAIN INSTEAD OF ME!

UUUUH?

ALAN LYNCH!

RIGHT! NOW TELL ME THAT ROY RACE CAN'T RECOGNISE TALENT WHEN HE SEES IT...

...BUT ALAN HAD SOMETHING ELSE GOING FOR HIM...

...DEDICATION AND COMMON SENSE! WHEN ROY GAVE ME THE SACK, HE DID ME A FAVOUR! HE MADE ME REALISE THAT IF I REALLY WANTED TO SUCCEED IN THIS GAME, I HAD TO GET MY HEAD DOWN AND START LEARNING MY TRADE! WHEN BURNDEAN GAVE ME A SECOND CHANCE, I DIDN'T WASTE IT!

B—BUT I THOUGHT... I MEAN— WHY HAVEN'T YOU SPOKEN LIKE THIS BEFORE, SON?

MAYBE HE DIDN'T WANT TO HURT YOU, MISTER DRAKE! ANYWAY, YOU CAN BE REALLY PROUD OF TERRY NOW...

...I'VE MET A LOT OF PEOPLE WHO THOUGHT THEY KNEW EVERYTHING ABOUT THIS GREAT GAME OF OURS...

...BUT IT'S NOT OFTEN YOU MEET SOMEONE WHO IS MAN ENOUGH TO ADMIT IT! YOU'RE A CREDIT TO FOOTBALL, TERRY DRAKE!

THE END

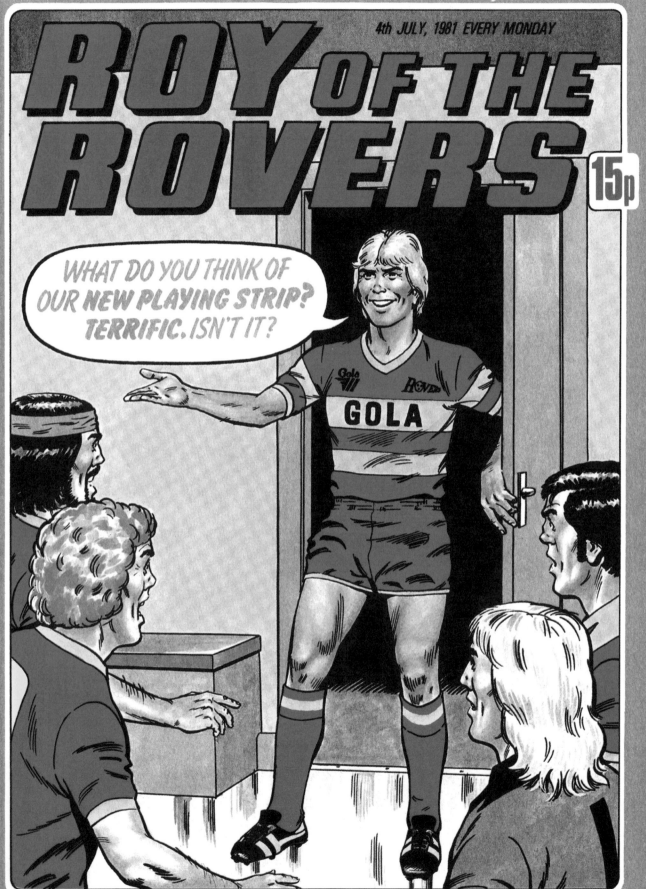

THE ROYAL WEDDING

1st AUGUST, 1981
EVERY MONDAY

15p

ROY OF THE ROVERS

Roy's tribute to His Royal Highness The Prince Of Wales and Lady Diana Spencer.

ROY AT THE ROYAL WEDDING!

©IPC Magazines Ltd., 1981

Australia 45c., New Zealand 45c., Malaysia $1.20., IR 21p (inc. VAT)

TOM TULLY

Tom Tully is one the most prolific writers ever to grace British comics. His diverse portfolio of work was produced over four decades. Born in Glasgow, Tully entered the industry in the sixties when he began working for Fleetway. One of his earliest strips, *Heros the Spartan*, ran in the original **Eagle** and was illustrated by the great Frank Bellamy. He also wrote *Mytek the Mighty* (**Valiant** & **Vulcan**) and *The Steel Claw* (**Valiant** & **Vulcan**) in the same decade.

The seventies saw Tully work on a variety of significant stories including *Adam Eterno* (**Thunder**), *Johnny Red* (**Battle**), *Harlem Heroes* (**2000 AD**), *The Leopard from Lime Street* (**Buster**) and *Roy of the Rovers* (**Tiger**), the strip he worked on longer than any other writer.

DAVID SQUE

A native of Bournemouth, David Sque studied at the Bournemouth Art College and got his National Diploma in Art and Design. He drew the car sports comic strip, *The Skids Kids* which appeared in **Buster** in the late 1960s. He illustrated *Martin's Marvellous Mini* in **Tiger**, but is best known for illustrating the *Roy of the Rovers* comic strip from January 1975 to August 1986 and was on art duties when the **Roy of the Rovers** comic book was launched in 1976. David's work on the strip was widely acclaimed. He would go on to illustrate another football strip - *Scorer*, which ran for several years in the **Daily Mirror** newspaper.

Over the years David has been in demand for his fine art paintings. He has also provided several technical illustrations for the Royal National Lifeboat Institution.